Olive's Diary

AN UNPUTDOWNABLE STORY ABOUT HOPE, LOSS AND SECOND CHANCES

Maiko Serizawa

Edited by Sonny Marr
Cover design by Ashley Santoro
Formatted by Tapioca Press

ISBN: 978-1-7782829-1-1 (e-book)
ISBN: 978-1-7782829-0-4 (paperback)

This book is dedicated to my little brother. Through his short but full life on earth, he taught me the value of life, the gift of seeing what cannot be seen with eyes, and the heart to love.

Contents

Chapter 1

Perspective Change

I t was a particularly beautiful Sunday morning. The blue of the sky was as clear as a crystal and the golden sunlight peeked through the old maple tree in the backyard as quietly and gently as the water of a mountain spring. Olive, still in her soft purple night gown, stepped out from her back door onto the patio barefoot, stood under the maple tree and looked up at her beloved friend.

Olive had saluted her tree every morning for over twenty years, ever since she moved into this house with her husband Robert and his daughter Lily. This tree had been what brought this family to the house twenty-one years ago. When the family visited the house for the first time, Olive and three-year-old Lily immediately fell in love with the old maple, and upon seeing their delight, Robert suggested that they should choose this house to be their forever home. Though many things had changed over the years; Lily's growing up and eventually moving out of the house for her studies, Robert's sudden passing, Olive's morning ritual remained unchanged.

1

Looking up at the branches, Olive could see some of the leaves starting to change their colour. Another summer had passed. September 22nd. It was on this day the previous year that Robert died of a heart attack. That day, Olive was having her morning coffee in exactly the same spot, and Robert came out to join her with a newspaper in his hand. Olive closed her eyes and took a sip of coffee from the mug in her hands.

"One year," she whispered to herself as if to feel the full weight of the 365 days that had passed, then let out a small sigh as she opened her eyes.

Riverside was a small rural city in Eastern Canada, hidden somewhere between the two provinces of Ontario and Quebéc. The city was an amalgamation of several former independent towns and had many distinct neighbourhoods. Among them was Olive's beloved Richmond. Richmond had always been Olive's favourite place to spend weekends. Being the hub of local businesses, the neighbourhood carried a particularly cheerful and uplifting atmosphere.

When Lily was young, Richmond meant treats. During summer, the family would often cycle to the small ice cream parlour on Main Street to get Lily's favourite strawberry flavour. After Lily went to college, Olive would look forward to a weekend date with Robert, which usually involved a lot of reading and conversation in one of the many local cafés. Olive would slightly dress up for the occasion, and the two of them would talk about what was going on in each other's life or share gems from their recent reading over coffee and pastries. After Robert's death, Olive still came back here to shop from time to time, and to find some comfort in this cheerful corner of town, sometimes accompanied by her good old friend Leila.

Olive had thought that Richmond was a place where nobody would feel alone, even if they did not have company, but as she stepped off the bus onto the busy street that afternoon, Olive was not consoled by the bustling crowd of happy faces. On the contrary, she felt totally at odds with the place.

Confused and suddenly not knowing which way to go, Olive stood there on the sidewalk, staring at the people passing by. A tiny lump formed in her throat, a ball of anxiety which seemed to grow bigger and spread until it reached every inch of her body. Before she knew it, Olive was pinned to the spot, unable to move.

"Breathe, Olive, breathe," she said to herself, as she attempted to control her panic attack before it overwhelmed her. She had not had one for several months, but the sensation was so familiar that it scared her. Olive quickly reached for her phone. The first face that came to her mind was Lily. For a split second, Olive's trembling finger hovered over Lily's number on her favourites contact list. Then she quickly shook her head to bat the thought away.

"Have you lost your mind, Olive?" Olive moved her shaking finger down to the next number and called Leila. She held onto the phone tight while the ringing tone continued.

"Oh, hi Leila," Olive stammered when she finally heard Leila's familiar voice pick up on the other end. "I think I've just had a panic attack, and needed to talk to somebody..." she explained, trying hard to pull herself together.

"Olive? Are you okay?" Leila's concerned voice rang in her ear. "Where are you, Olive?"

Olive looked around. On one level she knew exactly where she was, except that it now felt like a totally strange place.

"Olive, where are you?" Leila asked again. Olive could hear Leila picking up her keys.

"Oh, don't worry, Leila, there's no need to come," said

Olive quickly. "I just needed to talk to somebody. Hearing your voice, I already feel much better."

Olive tried to smile, but all she could do was flinch.

"Olive? You don't sound well. I'm coming to you right now."

There was a jingling sound of keys following Leila's words, then the sound of slippers flapping against the floor. Olive thought that Leila must be walking toward the door and she panicked.

"Leila, but I'm really fine." She lied. "I'll go now, I love you."

Olive hung up the call before Leila could answer.

Olive was furious at herself for her compulsive action. She knew Leila would be worried sick. It was a good thing that she did not call Lily at least. Upon thinking of Lily, Olive's heart sank. What was she thinking to call Lily in this situation? What was she going to tell her anyway?

Slowly and with no small effort, Olive started to pick her way through the crowd. The lump in her throat had now dissolved into a burning pain in her chest. She needed to find some place to sit. As she looked around in desperation, she saw a sign across the street. On a white wooden board, the name "Café Rose" was engraved in bright crimson lettering.

"Interesting," thought Olive. "Isn't this the place where Robby and I promised to visit when we were here together for the last time?"

The place was a French café bakery that opened a little over a year ago and had a good reputation, but they had never got around to going. Today it felt as if the coffee shop had been waiting for Olive's visit.

Café Rose stood at the corner where the bustling Main Street intersected with a narrow street. Facing a small park on the other side, the building carried a serene and peaceful atmosphere. Through the polished glass window, Olive could see a shiny brown wooden counter table decorated with flowers and other small plants. There were not many people to be seen inside except one young lady at the counter writing something in her notebook. Clearly the busy weekend afternoon rush was over so Olive could spend some quiet time while recovering from her panic attack.

A bell on the door tinkled above her as Olive pushed the front door open. As soon as she stepped inside, Olive was welcomed with the mixed smell of herbs, pastries, and ground coffee. The smell was so inviting that for a moment, Olive forgot about her panic attack. As she inhaled the fragrance, a tiny smile played on her lips.

"Hello, how can I help you?" A young lady in an apron approached her with a beaming smile. "You can have a seat wherever you want. Where would you like?"

Olive looked around uncertainly.

"Well..." Her gaze drifted to the counter table. The small plants on the table looked inviting, as did the view of the street. "I think I'll have a seat by the window."

Once settled at the table, Olive ordered a cappuccino and a croissant, her all-time favourite combination. After the waitress had taken her order and left, Olive took a deep breath. She was surprised by the turn of events and at the same time pleased that she was unexpectedly led to Café Rose on this very special day.

Right in front of her, there was a small pot of African violets with a handwritten tag that said "Please don't water the plant!" Olive smiled at the message. On the shelf next to her, there was a colourful display of porcelain cups and pots which looked as though they had been plucked straight from the

French countryside. Their polished surfaces sparkled under the decorative light hanging from the ceiling. In the background, she could hear the soft timbre of old French songs playing like the sound of waves on a beach.

Olive gazed out of the window. The street was still full of people, but she felt safe inside. From where she was sitting, everything looked more distant, almost like another world. Sitting opposite her on the counter was the young lady with the notebook, a pencil perched in her right hand. She seemed to be deep in thought. With her brow lightly furrowed, she stooped over her notebook, while her soft chestnut hair fell and gently covered her face. Every so often she paused to look up and stared into the distance as if she were listening to something that only she could hear.

The young lady's demeanour reminded Olive of Lily when she was a young girl and used to spend a lot of time drawing in the backyard. Lily would be so absorbed in her drawing that she was deaf to anything and everything else - not even pausing to notice when Olive stood right next to her. Olive remembered how it felt like such a privilege to look at her stepdaughter's masterpieces on the page before calling her in for a meal.

Now, Olive looked at the young lady intently and with the same curiosity that made her stay quiet and watch her step-daughter's drawing. Suddenly, Olive felt a gentle sting in her chest. Her heart longed for Lily, for the connection she had once had with her beloved stepdaughter.

The waitress came back with a cappuccino and a croissant for Olive, then made her way over to the girl with the notebook to ask if she wanted a refill of her coffee. She looked momentarily startled, but then gave the waitress a benevolent smile and nodded, her eyes still dreamy from contemplation.

Once the waitress had left with her mug, Olive watched as

the young lady reached for her pain au chocolat, took an elegant bite, then caught Olive's eyes on the other side of the table. Embarrassed, Olive straightened up and put on her best smile before apologizing.

"I'm sorry... I didn't mean to stare at you, but you just reminded me of my daughter when she was a little girl. You're so absorbed in your writing," said Olive nervously, hoping that her smile actually looked like one.

"Oh!" said the young lady, looking down at her notebook and then turning back to Olive. "Your daughter likes writing?"

"Well, she used to love drawing," said Olive. "She would spend hours drawing in our garden completely absorbed in her world. Just like you're with your writing."

"Did I look so absorbed?" said the young lady again, now blushing. Olive liked this young lady. There was something so honest and lively about her.

"Yes, and I'm truly sorry for interrupting you."

"Oh, don't be sorry," she replied. "I'm happy to know that I reminded you of your time with your daughter."

Olive smiled in reply, which did not last for long. Her eyesight was quickly blurred by tears and her throat was tightened by a pang of loneliness.

"I'm Olive, by the way," she said, as she blinked back the tears.

"I'm Maple," said the young lady.

"Maple? As in a maple tree?" Olive asked in surprise.

"That's right."

Olive took a sip from her cappuccino and a bite from her croissant. They were all the more comforting given the situation. Olive remembered Robert once telling her that Café Rose was most famous for its French pastries, including Olive's favourite, the croissants.

"This is actually my first time here," said Olive. "My husband and I found this place a year ago and planned to visit," she explained. "But we never made it... Actually, today is exactly one year since my husband passed away." Olive said the last sentence as quickly and lightly as possible.

When she looked up, her eyes met with Maple's. Instead of saying the dreaded words "I'm sorry to hear that," Maple nodded quietly. And after a brief pause, she slowly said, "Isn't it special that you're here today? I'm so happy that you finally made it."

That moment, something clicked inside Olive. It was like all of the strings that had been holding her together finally broke free from her grip. Tears streamed down Olive's cheeks. She did not know how long she sat like that. It could have been a few minutes, but it felt like a very long time. When she finally calmed down, she turned to Maple and smiled through her tears. Maple smiled back, gently placing her hand on Olive's arm.

The two of them sat in silence for a while. This time, Maple was the one to break it. "I come here every Sunday to write in my diary," she said, looking out of the window. "I like to reflect upon my week before starting a new one. I've been doing it for a few years now, and I must say my mental health has improved greatly ever since," she smiled at Olive. Olive wondered if she had known any smile that was as radiant and comforting as the one in front of her.

"What do you do in your life? For work I mean," asked Olive sipping her cappuccino.

"Oh, I'm a mathematician," said Maple casually. "I teach at Riverside College."

Olive's eyes widened with surprise. In front of Maple's smiling face, Olive tried to speak while still sipping her cappuccino and choked. Maple hurriedly reached for a napkin.

"Sorry!" Olive apologized as she received the napkin from Maple. "I was always terrible at math! My husband knew that more than anyone. I can read numbers, but that's about it. Big numbers are definitely not for me! When we married, one condition I asked for was that he would be in charge of the family finance because there was no way I could deal with that." Olive took a sip of cappuccino and continued. "Now that he's gone, my good friends help. I'm really hopeless with math. I couldn't even imagine being a mathematician!" she said with a laugh.

Perhaps Maple saw Olive's left hand clutching her skirt tightly. Her eyes softened as if feeling for Olive's discomfort tucked under all this speech.

"Well, you can forget that I'm a mathematician," said Maple gently. "I don't want to make you feel uncomfortable. Just think of me as somebody who writes her diary every Sunday at Café Rose."

Olive let out a sigh of relief. "Well, that makes me feel more relaxed."

The waitress came back with Maple's coffee. A moment of silence fell as they both helped themselves to the last piece of their pastries.

"When I woke up this morning, I had no idea I'd come here and meet you today," said Olive abruptly, gazing at the people outside. "You know, I was really in a bad shape earlier. I'd just had a panic attack on the street before coming here. I was on the verge of collapsing when I saw this place and ran inside."

"Oh my gosh," Maple looked at Olive with eyes full of concern. "You had a panic attack on the street? I didn't realize that when you first came in. I'm so sorry. Are you okay?"

"I'm fine now." Olive smiled. It was an effortless smile that came from her heart. "Strangely enough, I feel so different now.

Calm and happy. Even the street outside looks different to me. Less overwhelming."

"Perspective change," said Maple. "The same thing can look different when we change our perspective."

It was a throwaway remark but it captured Olive's attention. She wanted to hear more about it. As if noticing Olive's keen expression, Maple took her empty plate and placed it between them.

"What shape does this look like?" Maple asked. Surprised by the sudden question, Olive answered.

"A circle?" Then she hurriedly corrected herself. "Well, it's a little distorted. So, should I call it an oval?"

Maple nodded, then pushed the plate closer to Olive.

"How about now?"

"Still the same, though it's less distorted."

"Now what if you look at it from straight above?"

"Then it's a proper circle." Olive answered with confidence. Maple picked up the plate and raised it to Olive's eye level.

"Now, what shape does this look like?"

Olive looked at the plate, then looked at Maple, who now had a mischievous smile on her face.

"It now looks like a... kind of like a very thin rectangle to me," said Olive.

"Would you recognize that it's a plate if I'd shown it to you from this angle only?"

"No," answered Olive honestly, "I wouldn't."

Maple placed the plate back on the table and sipped her coffee with a triumphant expression on her face.

"This is a small experiment to show a perspective change. You can see its subtlety and impact," said Maple. "You might be wondering 'So *what?*' And you have every right to feel that way," she continued. "After all, everybody knows that a plate looks different from different angles. But a fascinating thing about perspective change is," she said, turning to Olive, "that once we become really aware of it, we can start to look for perspective changes in whatever circumstance that we find ourselves in. Even when a perspective isn't so obvious."

Maple said quietly, resting her hands on the notebook. "I always try to remember that in my life."

Olive dropped her gaze, pondering Maple's words and saw on her watch that it was almost five o'clock. The waitress was clearing away the outside seating on the street.

"They're closing soon," said Maple, sipping her last drip of coffee and putting her diary into her bag. "I guess we should be going."

Olive stretched her arms and realized how light her body now felt. "It was so lovely meeting you, Maple," she said whole-heartedly and extended her hand.

"Oh, I also had a great time talking with you." Maple beamed as she shook Olive's hand. "I'm here every Sunday. So, if you decide to come again, you'll probably find me here!"

"That would be lovely." Olive smiled.

On the way back home, Olive dropped by at a large grocery chain on Main Street. At the entrance, a bouquet of pink roses caught her eye, and she decided to buy it to celebrate the day and commemorate the anniversary of Robert's departure.

As she waited for her bus, Olive took out her phone and found a series of text messages from Leila asking if she was okay. There were also several missed calls. Olive's phone had been on silent mode, and she had not thought of checking it until now.

For all this time, Leila must have been worried to death thinking of Olive. A sense of guilt gushed through Olive's body. Olive called Leila right away, and when the call went to voice-mail, she left a brief message, thanking Leila for calling and reassuring her that she was now really fine and on her way home.

On top of the fact that Olive stayed at the grocery store longer than she had planned, her bus did not arrive soon. By the time Olive reached home, the sun had started to set, flaring up one side of the sky in pink while leaving the other side turn into a river of dark blue flowing into the vastness of the night that was about to begin.

As she walked up to the door, Olive noticed a brown paper bag left on the doorstep. It contained handmade lemon biscuits accompanied by a handwritten note.

Dear Olive,

I hope you are feeling better now. I tried calling you, but you didn't answer. I got so worried that I would have visited all the hospitals in town if Alan hadn't stopped me! I needed to do something to calm myself down, so I baked you Robby's favourite biscuits. Hope you're okay.

Love, Leila

The biscuits were still warm. Leila must have just come by. Olive was touched by her friend's deep sense of care and felt sorry again for having kept her worrying all afternoon.

After dinner, Olive placed the pink roses in a vase on her nightstand and made herself a hot cup of rooibos tea. In her purple nightgown, she sat by the window of her bedroom with her favourite Peter Rabbit mug and Leila's lemon biscuits.

"What an amazing day it was," Olive spoke softly to herself. "Well, Robby, I did have a great day today, to my surprise."

She looked out of the window. Her beloved tree was

swaying gently in the wind, accompanied by a soothing sound of rustling leaves.

"Remember the coffee place we talked about visiting last year? Well, guess what? I finally went there, and met a wonderful young lady. You've got to meet her, Robby." Olive sighed and closed her eyes. "She reminded me of our Lily."

Chapter 2

Problem

It was 9 pm. Olive had removed her slippers and sat on the bed with her phone beside her when she heard a familiar ringtone. It was from Lily.

Olive's heart bounced with joy as she reached for her phone. She was reminded how much she had missed Lily for all this time.

"Lily, my dear!" Olive heard an excitement in her own voice as she picked up the call. "How wonderful is it that you called me tonight!"

There was an awkward silence.

"Your dad's one year anniversary..." Olive started to say, but Lily interrupted.

"Mom, I'm sorry that I wasn't with you today." Before Olive could say anything, she continued. "I really wanted to be with you today, but I really couldn't come."

Olive looked at the wall in front of her. Her maple tree was casting a pattern of shades, moving quietly in the darkness. "Lily, my dear, you don't need to feel sorry," said Olive at last. "I know you're busy and work won't let you take many days off." Lily was silent and Olive worried that she had somehow said the wrong thing.

"Are you doing well?" Olive continued, trying to put on a cheerful voice.

"I'm all right," said Lily quickly, then paused. "How about you, Mom? How was your day?"

Olive thought for a moment. The fresh memory of her day came back to her with a surge of excitement.

"I had a wonderful day. I tried a new coffee place in Richmond." She was careful not to mention that it was a panic attack that led her there. "It's a place where your dad and I once planned to visit."

"Was it nice?" asked Lily. Realizing that she had piqued her daughter's interest, Olive eagerly continued.

"Oh, yes! It's a lovely French bakery called Café Rose. Remember that ice cream parlour? Your favourite, the one we used to visit every summer? It's in the same block facing the corner park. The place is cozy, with pretty plants and some old French songs. I sat at the counter table by the window, and became friends with a lovely young lady!"

Olive told Lily about her encounter with Maple, how they chatted over delicious pastries and how she was inspired by their conversation. It had been a while since Olive talked with Lily on the phone, and she could not help feeling elated. Moreover, Canadian Thanksgiving was just around the corner. In a few weeks, Olive would be able to see Lily in person.

"Now, you can tell me about your day, my dear," said Olive once her story came to an end. "I mean, I could wait until you come here for Thanksgiving, but I'd prefer to hear it now!" She chuckled.

Suddenly, there was silence, before Lily cleared her throat.

"Well, about that..." said Lily slowly. Her voice was now tense. "Mom, I'm sorry, but I won't be coming this time."

There was a pause. Olive felt as if somebody had punctured her heart with a needle. Like a balloon, her buoyant mood at speaking to her daughter began to deflate quickly. She needed a moment to register what she had just heard.

"Lily, my dear..." Olive opened her mouth without knowing exactly what to say. When she finally spoke, her voice came out thin and fragile. "You're really not coming home for Thanksgiving?"

"I'm so sorry, Mom. I couldn't take the long weekend off. I have some work to do."

Is it because of your work, or is it because of me? The question swirled in Olive's head like a cold breeze. She was speechless. Lily apologized again, her voice sounding rigid and awkward.

"You don't need to feel sorry, my dear." Olive tried her best to pull herself together when everything inside of her was about to collapse. "It's just that I was so looking forward to seeing you, and I wasn't quite prepared for not having you for Thanksgiving."

"I'm sorry." Lily repeated.

After hanging up the call, Olive lay down on her bed and stared out of the window. It was amazing how the tree and the sky looked different from this angle. Olive closed her eyes. Her eyes were burning and her breath was shaking. As she pushed her wet cheeks into the pillow, she wondered what possible perspective change could save her from this misery tonight.

The next morning, Olive woke up to the sound of pouring rain. She could hear the raindrops hitting the roof, tapping on the leaves of her maple tree and thundering to the ground. The air must have cooled during the night because she could hear the hot air from the automatic heater billowing through the vent.

Olive slowly put on the house slippers that she kept on the rug beside the bed and started to wander around the room, getting herself ready for work. As she rummaged through her closet for some warm clothes, she came across her favourite piece - her rose pink trench coat. Olive had not worn it for a while. It was much louder than what Olive would usually wear. Robert had bought it for her several years ago as a birthday present. He had chosen it knowing how much she loved the colour, but would never have bought the piece for herself. *This will make me happy today*, smiled Olive.

Half an hour later, Olive was standing at the bus stop dressed in her rose pink trench coat, holding her decade old white floral umbrella. The rain had lightened up a little, but the road was full of dirt and deep puddles. Olive carefully stayed away from the curb so that the cars would not splash dirty droplets on her favourite coat.

Every morning, Olive commuted to the Rosemary Public Library by bus, where she worked as a librarian. It was a pleasant bus ride, just twenty minutes from her house through a sequence of well-maintained neighbourhoods. Usually, Olive would either enjoy the view from the window or read a book during her journey. But as soon as she got on the bus that morning, Olive's thoughts drifted to the conversation she had with Lily the night before.

Olive was surprised by her emotional reaction to the news that Lily was not coming home for Thanksgiving. Since Robert's death, Lily had cancelled many visits home and Olive had been fine each time. But this time, it was different. On top of the fact that the previous day had been emotional, Olive felt disappointed and hurt. There was also a layer of anxiety beneath it.

"Oh, come on, Olive," Olive pinched her hand and whispered to herself. "Lily is an adult. She has her own life. You cannot expect her to be around you all the time." But then, she could not neglect the vast sadness that spread across her body.

When she got off the bus in front of the Library, Olive was still so deep in thought that she did not see the truck approaching her. She jerked when the driver honked at her, and jumped back to the sidewalk just in time to avoid a collision. As she tried to balance herself, the truck drove through a large pothole and a big splash of muddy water showered on her. She was drenched, and her beautiful rose pink trench coat was now miserably spoiled by the muddy water. Olive wanted to cry, but she was startled when something hit her hard in the back and slammed her to the ground. There was a sharp pain in her left arm, and Olive felt her body sink in the water before she lost consciousness.

When Olive woke up, she found herself in a doctor's office. Her entire body was aching, and her left arm was covered by something hard. As she tried to move, a female doctor appeared from the corner of her eye and beamed at her.

"You woke up, my dear?" She smiled and helped Olive to slowly sit up on the bed. The doctor appeared to be in her fifties and had a kind voice.

"Now dear, would you mind answering these questions for me? What is your name?"

"Olive. Olive Melrose."

"How old are you?"

"Fifty-six."

"Where do you live?"

"Bayview Street, Riverside."

"And what day is it today?"

Olive thought for a while. "23rd September."

"Perfect," said the doctor writing down on her notebook. Then she turned to Olive.

"You had an accident, Olive. This morning, a cyclist bumped into you and you fell on the road. Your colleagues have carried you here."

Olive nodded, trying to remember the scene.

"Unfortunately, the cyclist didn't stop. By the time you were found they were already gone. But we can file a case for the police if you wish."

"Am I badly injured?" Olive asked. The doctor told her that she had broken her wrist, but that was all.

"We checked that there was no major internal injury except for the broken wrist. You were truly fortunate, Olive. You must have protected yourself when you fell on the ground." Olive nodded again. The doctor said that it would take about six weeks for her wrist to heal.

"I don't need to file the case for the police," said Olive in a determined voice. "I was being careless in the first place, and now I know that my injury isn't too bad..." The doctor asked her if she was absolutely sure. "Yes, I'm sure about it." Olive replied.

She was allowed to leave the clinic before noon with her arm secured in a splint. As she slowly walked through the hallway toward the entrance, a familiar figure came running from the opposite direction. It was Leila.

"Olive, OLIVE!" Leila panted and exclaimed as she came within earshot. Her long hair was dancing everywhere and the top of her purse was flapping frantically with each step she took.

"Oh, my goodness, Olive," said Leila again as she reached Olive and carefully embraced her right shoulder. She must have been in the midst of painting when she left home. Olive could see streaks of green in Leila's black hair. "Your colleague called me and told me about your accident," said Leila. "Oh, Olive, you have no idea how scared I was! You had a panic attack yesterday, and today an accident? My mind went blank and I just jumped onto my car. I didn't even *think* whether you'd still be here or not." She took a breath and looked at Olive. "You're alive."

Seeing tears in her friend's shiny turquoise eyes, Olive wondered if things could have been worse.

"I'm sorry, Leila. But I'm okay now. I've only broken my wrist."

Olive had planned to catch a bus outside, but the two of them drove back to Olive's house together in Leila's car. On the way, Olive explained to her what had happened that morning, with as much detail as she could remember. She explained how she was distracted and how her rose pink trench coat was ruined by the puddle water splashed by a truck, how she was so preoccupied by the water marks that she did not realize when a cyclist hit her. Leila listened to her breathlessly. When Olive told her about the moment she fell on the ground, she let out an audible gasp.

"Olive, *please* promise me that you'll be more careful in the future!" exclaimed Leila when Olive finished her tale. "I can't bear the thought of something happening to you. You know how much I love you, Olive. And think of Lily. How would *she* manage if something terrible happened to you after losing her father like that?"

Olive looked at her pale reflection in the front window. She had not thought of that.

"I'll be more careful, Leila. I promise."

"Thank you!"

Leila turned the handle, and the car steered away from Riverside Avenue onto a quiet neighbourhood street.

"Did you call Lily yet?" asked Leila.

"Lily?" Olive stammered. "I'm not planning to tell her about this accident." Before Leila could say anything, she added. "Lily's got a lot on her mind at the moment. She's busy with her work, and it's an emotional time what with the anniversary being yesterday. I don't want her to worry about me."

Leila looked slightly skeptical. "So will you wait until Thanksgiving to tell her in person?"

"She's not coming this time."

"She's not coming?!" Leila pressed hard on the brake and the car came to a sudden halt in front of Olive's house.

"Careful Leila! I've already been in the hospital once today."

"Sorry! I was just so shocked that Lily isn't coming home."

An uneasy silence fell in the car.

"Lily called me yesterday and told me that she can't make it this Thanksgiving." Olive tried to sound as casual as possible.

"But it's been nine months since she last saw you."

"I know." Olive smiled faintly. "But she's busy, Leila. What can I do? I don't want to be in her way."

Leila did not say anything. Her expression showed that she was not convinced by Olive's explanation and that she did not believe Olive herself was convinced either. Leila opened her mouth, then closed it quickly as if determined to hold back her questions. Instead, she offered to come in and prepare lunch for Olive, but Olive gently turned it down, saying that she wanted some rest just by herself.

"I cannot thank you enough for your help today, Leila. I would've gotten into even more trouble without you." Kissing

21

her friend goodbye, Olive remembered something else. "And thank you also for the lemon biscuits yesterday!"

Leila laughed. "At *least* you allow your old friend to bake your favourite biscuits for you!"

Olive got off the car and started to walk toward her house. She could feel that Leila was watching her to make sure that she actually went inside the house. As she turned the lock and opened the door, Olive heard Leila start the engine. Then she heard Leila shout from the window.

"Olive! Don't forget how much you mean to the people around you! Not just the other way around!"

Olive turned and smiled. She waved Leila off with her good arm and watched her friend's car until it slowly disappeared from her sight.

The week went by slowly. Olive took an absence of leave from work and spent her time at home. It was not a decision she preferred, but her thoughtful boss insisted that Olive should take at least a few days off after the accident and rest at home. Though Olive's job at the library was not hugely demanding, it had been her saviour throughout the past year, keeping her busy and getting her out of the house. Olive dreaded to be alone in the house with nothing much to do.

It reminded Olive of the weeks after Robert's funeral. In order to avoid her overwhelming emotions, Olive started to deep clean the house. She needed to do it anyway before Thanksgiving, so she might as well do it now.

As she organized the clutter, collecting books and clothes for donation, sweeping and mopping the floor using her good, right hand, her mind was momentarily distracted from the memory of last year, but one thought kept coming back. *Lily is not coming for Thanksgiving.* Then her mind would drift off, as it often did when she was alone, to the long list of things she had not done right since Robert's death.

Each night of her enforced vacation, Olive collapsed on the bed completely exhausted, feeling lost and tearful. The only thing that kept her going that week was the thought of her visiting Café Rose again on Sunday. Olive remembered the cozy ambience, the taste of the flaky croissant and the cappuccino, and the conversation with Maple. Maple said that she wrote in her diary every Sunday there. *If the occasion allowed,* thought Olive, *it would be nice to see her again.*

When Sunday finally arrived after much anticipation, instead of taking a bus, Olive took a long walk to Richmond. After an hour walking through the neighbourhoods, Olive reached Main Street. She continued walking through the bustling crowd of people and many inviting shop fronts until she finally came to the corner where her beloved café stood.

Café Rose was busier than last time. As she stepped inside, Olive was welcomed by chattering voices and the tinkling sound of plates and glasses. The room was filled with the now familiar smell of fresh bread, soups and coffee from the lunch tables.

As Olive nervously looked around wondering if she had arrived a little too early, she found an empty spot at the end of the counter table. Since the waiters were busy, and feeling a little bold, Olive decided to seat herself. She squeezed herself through the merry customers, into the right corner of the counter table next to the display of gleaming pots and cups.

When a waitress finally found Olive and came to take her order, she ordered a cappuccino and a croissant. Then, there was nothing more to do. At home, this was where she would normally derail into the never-ending list of things she had done wrong. But here at Café Rose, Olive felt too happy to go to that place. Instead, she turned her curious gaze to the people walking on the street outside. She observed the different families and friends and wondered what kind of week they might have had. She inhaled the fragrance of the food and coffee around her and fantasized about the lunch menus the people around her must have enjoyed today. She then focused on listening to the French song in the background and tapped her finger on the wooden table mat along with the music. As she tapped, the table mat slightly shifted, and something white became visible from its edge. The white thing looked like a piece of paper.

"Somebody has forgot something here." Intrigued, Olive pulled it out. It was a postcard with a most breathtaking view of the seaside at sunset, with a pale blue ocean and a golden sand beach. From the colour of the water and the houses nearby, Olive guessed that it belonged to one of the Mediterranean countries. She flipped the card. There was nothing written on the other side. Somebody must have planned to write a postcard here and left it.

"Oh, shame," said Olive. She was about to put it back under the table mat when she suddenly remembered how Robert used to love talking about the Mediterranean countries and their beautiful seaside. When they first got together, he promised Olive to one day take her on a trip to the Mediterranean, visiting many historic cites together, meeting local people and discovering local cuisines. A dream that was never fulfilled.

Olive took a closer look at the picture. Under the setting sun, people were enjoying their time on the quiet sand beach. A wave of pale blue water garnished with white bubbles gently caressed the shore, and behind the sand beach stood a series of colourful buildings auspiciously reflecting the amber sunlight.

Olive wondered what it would have been like to walk on

this sand beach with Robert, listening to the sound of waves and people's voices in the distance, amazed by everything new they were discovering together. Unlike Robert, Olive was never a big traveller, and she was afraid of flying, which made travelling oversees difficult. During their twenty years of their marriage, Olive always made sure that wherever they travelled was accessible by land. Vehicles with wheels were the only travelling method Olive could handle. Robert never complained about it, but deep down, Olive knew he had dreamed of a bigger adventure for them.

"I'm going to keep it. Do you mind?" Olive spoke to whoever had left this card under her table mat, then put the card into her handbag.

When Olive looked up, she saw a familiar figure walking back from the bathroom. It was Maple.

"Olive!" Her face lit up as she waved at Olive. "I didn't notice that you were here!"

"Neither did I!" said Olive, surprised and delighted at the same time.

"Oh, I'm so happy you came, Olive. I was actually hoping to see you today. I really enjoyed meeting you last time!" Maple beamed. A drop of warmth rippled across Olive's heart, making her almost shiver.

"So did I," said Olive. "I was thinking today that if I were lucky, I would see you again at Café Rose. Have you already finished writing your diary?"

"Oh, yes. I have been sitting here for a while now. I've written quite a few pages, and I'm feeling really good."

Maple sat on her chair and faced Olive. The elderly couple who had been sitting between them had left some time ago, and the whole table now belonged to the two of them.

Today, Maple was wearing a yellow sweater with a stylish

pair of red pants. On the front of her sweater, there was a quote. *A problem is the beginning of everything.*

"Nice quote," said Olive pointing at the sweater. Maple looked at it, and grinned.

"You like it? It's one of my favourites."

"I certainly have plenty of problems." Olive had meant it to be a joke, but it ended up sounding sad. She looked at Maple anxiously, but Maple was distracted by something else.

"Olive, what happened to your arm?" Maple's eyes were fixed on the splint covering Olive's left arm.

"Oh, this?" Olive tried to speak in a casual tone. "I broke my wrist earlier this week. I fell on the ground."

Maple clasped her mouth. "Oh, my! How did it happen?"

Olive would have loved not to go into detail, but she did anyway.

When she said that she never found out who hit her that morning, Maple became upset. "How can anybody hit and injure somebody and just run away like that?" Then she asked Olive what had happened to her rose pink trench coat.

"Well, I've left it with a professional laundry service. They warned me that it might not recover to its original state." Looking at Olive's disappointment, Maple reached her hand for Olive's. Olive smiled with a sigh.

"It's a good lesson not to be too caught up with belongings. Besides, I made a poor decision of wearing such a precious piece in such a terrible weather. In any case, now you know how hopelessly clumsy I am," said Olive, concluding her story.

"Well, it can happen to anybody, Olive." Maple looked at Olive seriously. "Especially when we are preoccupied with thoughts."

Olive felt uneasy.

"You're right, I was preoccupied," confessed Olive. "And actually, that's my real problem."

"That you were preoccupied?"

"No, I mean what I was distracted by." Olive looked out of the window, not certain how to explain what she was about to say.

"Well, the day I first met you, later that night my daughter called and told me that she's not coming home for Thanksgiving." Olive took a deep breath. "And frankly speaking, I'm devastated."

The moment Olive said it, a mixture of relief and shame enveloped her. She felt foolish to be disappointed by such a small matter. Lily was not coming home for Thanksgiving. What on earth was there to be so upset about?

When Olive looked up, she was met with Maple's thoughtful gaze.

"What's her name?" asked Maple.

"Lily."

"What a lovely name!" Maple exclaimed wholeheartedly making Olive smile. Even at her lowest point, it never failed to please Olive to see somebody delighted by her precious Lily.

"Where does she live?"

"Toronto. She went to college there, and now she works at a design studio."

"Wow, how amazing is that!"

Olive looked at Maple, whose eyes were now round with excitement. Maple's lively presence made Olive feel strangely younger than herself, and as much as it embarrassed her, she liked that feeling.

"I was really looking forward to seeing her after such a long time." Olive confessed. "So, the news of her not coming really put me down."

"How about *you* go and visit her in Toronto, then?"

Maple's suggestion caught Olive off guard, and it took a

27

moment for her brain to process what she had just heard. But when it did, Olive shook her head.

"Oh, no, I can't do that, Maple."

"Why not?"

Pressed by Maple's puzzled look, Olive thought hard for the reason. Why could she not go and visit Lily? Olive thought of Lily working at her busy design studio, how she was not picking up Olive's calls these days, and how she had cancelled her Thanksgiving visit during their last conversation. A sense of emptiness formed in Olive's chest. Looking back at Maple, Olive forced a sentence.

"Because she's busy with her work. She wouldn't want me to come."

"How do you know?" Maple's simple question pierced Olive like a sharp knife. Olive looked down, completely at a loss. Her heart was racing. Maple must have noticed this because she quickly apologized.

"I'm sorry, Olive. I feel I've been intrusive," said Maple with regret in her voice. "I just thought your daughter would be happy if you visited her. I never meant to hurt you. Forgive me if I did."

No, you didn't hurt me, it's my problem, Olive wanted to say, but she was too overwhelmed by the shock of her internal earthquake. Not knowing what to say, Olive pointed to Maple's yellow sweater instead.

"Tell me Maple, is that true? Is a problem the beginning of everything, not the end?" Maple was puzzled for a second, but when she understood what Olive was talking about, she smiled.

"Yes, it is." Seeing Olive's desperate expression, she added. "More accurately, a problem is an invitation to a new journey. Something that will allow us to experience a perspective change in the end. So, it's something to be celebrated when a person finds a new problem."

Olive held her cappuccino in her right hand and smiled faintly. "Then please let's celebrate, Maple. I have a big problem right now."

Maple looked surprised, but soon her surprise was replaced by a warm smile. They made a toast with their coffees. Olive laughed. Other than the fact that she now slightly felt better about herself, she had no idea how she had just set foot on a completely new journey.

The time had flown by, and it was again almost closing time at Café Rose. The waitress in a white apron was mopping the floor behind them. Olive sipped the last drop of her cold cappuccino and turned to Maple.

"How are you going to spend Thanksgiving, Maple? Are you going to visit your family?"

"Oh, no, I'll stay in town, I might visit a pumpkin patch. I heard it's really fun and I've never tried it," smiled Maple as she put away her diary and reached for her jacket. "My family live in Japan. It's too far to visit for a weekend."

"Japan?"

Olive lost her words for a second in surprise.

"Maple, are you... are you from Japan?"

"Oh, no, I'm not!" laughed Maple and waved her hand. "My mother's from Japan though. My family went back and forth when I was growing up, but we mostly lived in Vancouver until I was fifteen."

Olive looked at Maple in admiration. For Olive, who spent her entire life on one side of the country, Vancouver felt like a far-away place, let alone Japan.

"My parents moved to Japan when I was fifteen, but I decided to stay. I lived with my grandparents until I graduated high school, then went to college, and came to Toronto for my graduate studies. I came to Riverside about two years ago," said

Maple and smiled. Then she quickly added. "So, to conclude, I don't have much family here."

Olive was speechless for a moment, taking in all of what she had just heard from Maple. She had no idea that Maple and her family had travelled so far.

"Maple, would you like to come over to my house for Thanksgiving?"

The sentence came out of Olive's mouth before she knew it.

"You know, I'm thinking of inviting two of my very close friends, and it would be lovely if you could also join us."

Maple stared at Olive in surprise.

"That's so kind of you, Olive. But are you sure?"

"Of course! We would all love to have you there," said Olive, then quickly added. "If you don't mind having a dinner with three old people, that is!"

"Oh, I would love that, Olive! I honestly would!"

Maple held both hands together in front of her chest, her eyes twinkling like stars. Olive wrote down her address and phone number on a piece of paper and handed it to Maple.

"Here is my address and phone number. The bus route 56 stops right in front of my house, and if you drive, there is enough parking space for everyone because I don't have a car."

"Thank you so much!" said Maple as she carefully tucked the piece of paper into her pocket. "This is the very first Thanksgiving invitation that I've received from somebody outside of my family! I'm now too excited to wait for two more weeks!"

As Maple and Olive left Café Rose and parted ways, a sense of warmth filled Olive's heart. Olive walked to the bus stop and inhaled the fresh evening air before texting Leila about her new plan for Thanksgiving.

Chapter 3

Prompts

Thanksgiving Monday was a bright sunny day, the first welcome respite after a week of heavy rain. The growing patches of burnt orange and ruby red in the trees suggested that the peak of autumn's beauty was just around the corner. The air was crisp and noticeably cooler than it had been a few weeks ago, and a sense of stillness had descended. Occasionally a few leaves fell from Olive's tree, dancing through the gentle wind and landing on the ground ever so quietly that nobody would notice their departure.

Olive was working on final preparations for Thanksgiving dinner. She checked the temperature of the turkey in the oven and the colour of the roast potatoes as they crisped and sizzled next to it. Olive's continuous effort over the past two weeks had rendered the house spotless. The long wooden dining table was covered by a soft moss green tablecloth with embroidered olive branches. As she removed her apron and stood in her favourite lavender dress, Olive was pleasantly surprised by the quality of her preparation. It was the first dinner party that she had hosted alone since her marriage, and she had been skeptical of her capacity to manage all the preparation on her own.

Just before five, the doorbell rang and Maple arrived at the doorstep. Dressed in a dark brown jacket and dark blue jeans with her hair tied into an elegant ponytail, she beamed and embraced Olive into a gentle hug as soon as she opened the door.

"I'm so happy to see you, Olive. Thank you for inviting me today!" exclaimed Maple.

"I'm so glad that you're here," replied Olive, hiding the surge of emotion she felt all of a sudden. "Here, let me take your jacket."

When Maple removed her jacket, her bright orange sweater caught Olive's eye. She could not help looking for another quote on Maple's sweater, but there was none today. The orange sweater was plain except for the little pumpkin motif on her chest.

Without noticing Olive's curious gaze, Maple held out a basket of tiny pumpkins.

"Happy Thanksgiving! I actually visited a local pumpkin patch earlier today and thought these would be great decorations for the dinner table."

Six tiny pumpkins of different colours peeked from the basket.

"How adorable!" exclaimed Olive. "Thank you, Maple. The table definitely needs some decoration," smiled Olive and motioned Maple inside.

"Have you ever been to a pumpkin patch before?" asked Maple as she followed Olive into the dining room. Olive thought for a while.

"The last time I went was when I was seven or eight. There weren't these cute decorative pumpkins back then. I guess things have changed quite a bit."

"It was much more fun than I'd thought," said Maple excitedly, "looking at different shapes of pumpkins! Perhaps you can join me next time."

Olive turned to Maple and smiled.

"I might do that, Maple. I should get out of my house more and explore new things."

Together, Maple and Olive started to set the table for dinner. The room was getting dark, and Olive turned on the light. Maple decorated the table with the little pumpkins and tealights while Olive took out the turkey and the roast potatoes from the oven and carefully transferred them to plates.

"What a beautiful tablecloth you have," said Maple as she delicately placed her fingers on the embroidered olive branches. Olive smiled.

"My mother made it. It was our wedding gift."

"Wow, your mother is so professional!" exclaimed Maple in awe. "I mean, look at these details!"

Olive stopped what she was doing in the kitchen and looked at her familiar tablecloth.

"I guess you're right. She did a great job, didn't she? I'm sure she would have greatly appreciated your compliment if she were still alive."

Olive walked over to the table and pointed to the embroidered olive branches.

"You see these olives? My mother chose this pattern because my name is Olive."

"How sweet of your mother."

The two of them stood there in silence for a while before Olive remembered that they had not yet finished the dinner preparation. Maple carried the heavy dishes to the table, and Olive laid plates, glasses and cutlery.

The table was properly set when the doorbell rang for the second time.

"That's my friend Leila and Alan," smiled Olive. Before she finished her sentence however, the door flung open, and Leila marched in with open arms.

"Olive!" she exclaimed and held Olive tight in her arms. Olive had to loosen her left arm to prevent it from being squashed. "So good to see you, my dear! Happy Thanksgiving!"

Next to Leila stood a middle-aged man in a red sweater with a big warm smile, holding a brown paper bag and a bouquet of orange lilies.

"My dear Olive," said Alan as he gently hugged Olive and kissed on her cheek. "Thank you for inviting us. Happy Thanksgiving."

Alan held out the bouquet and the paper bag to Olive, then stopped, noticing the support on Olive's left arm. "Here, let me carry them to the kitchen. Your arm's still recovering."

"Oh, Alan, she's much better now," Leila jumped in. "When I first saw her in the hospital, her whole arm was covered in a splint. That accident was most..." started Leila, but Olive quickly reached for the brown paper bag interrupting Leila.

"Aren't these your biscuits, Leila? What biscuits have you baked this time?"

"My special pumpkin biscuits, of course," answered Leila, looking surprised. "But this time, I added a few different spices."

"Oh, Leila, I can't wait to try them!"

Smiling at Olive's excitement, Leila looked around the room. That was when she saw Maple for the first time. "Olive, is this young lady your...?"

Olive cleared her throat.

"Leila, Alan," started Olive eagerly. "Please meet my friend Maple. Maple, this is my dear old friend Leila and her husband

Alan. Leila and I went to school together, and Alan and my husband were high school classmates. We're truly old friends."

"And you know what that means?" remarked Leila in an excited voice. "We probably know each other's life more than we'd like to. Olive can't stand it whenever I worry too much about her because when that happens, I don't even give her enough breathing space!" Leila rolled her eyes.

"But Riverside is a small town. It's inevitable." Alan added thoughtfully. "And may I say, that's actually what I love about my life here?"

Maple looked at the three middle-aged friends in front of her, her eyes twinkling with curiosity.

"Truly a pleasure to meet you," said Maple extending her hand, which Leila shook enthusiastically.

"I've heard a lot about you, Maple," said Leila breathlessly. "Olive tells me about the conversations she has with you on Sundays. She's very fond of you." Leila's big kind eyes looked keenly into Maple's.

"Olive told me that you teach at Riverside College. But I don't seem to remember what..."

"Mathematics," said Maple smiling. "I'm a mathematician."

"A *mathematician*?" exclaimed Leila in a total surprise, her big eyes becoming even bigger. "For goodness' sake, she's a mathematician! Of all the decades I've known you, Olive, who could have imagined that you'd one day become friends with a mathematician?"

"I know," laughed Olive. "I do think the day I met Maple was one of the most unusual days of my life."

"Olive has never been great at math," explained Leila to Maple. "Sorry Olive, I don't mean to be rude."

"No offence taken Leila, I'll be the first to admit it!" answered Olive, laughing in the kitchen.

Leila continued. "Lots of people struggle with math, but Olive is different... She *suffered.*"

Maple nodded carefully.

"It started way back in grade 2 or 3, when we were learning the multiplication table. Olive is such a smart woman as you know, but she was never good at memorizing numbers. And you can't do much math if you can't handle numbers, can you?"

Maple was quiet.

"Anyway, all I know is that when we graduated from high school, Olive banished math from her life altogether. She can read numbers, but doesn't deal with them any further. Am I right, Olive?"

Maple looked at Olive. Olive laughed as she carried the vase of orange lilies from the kitchen and placed it on the dinner table.

"I've already told the story to Maple, Leila. Thank you for giving her more details. Now, can we please talk about something else? And, take a seat everyone, the food is ready."

"What do you do for work, Leila? If you don't mind me asking?" asked Maple politely as she sat across from Leila at the dinner table while Olive began to pour wine into everybody's glass.

"Oh, there's no need to be polite with us, Maple." Leila waved her hand. "I'm an artist. More specifically, I draw and paint. Alan is a writer. He writes stories for young children. I do illustration for his books, too."

"We make a good team," smiled Alan next to her.

As the feasting began and the food and alcohol put everybody in a happy mood, conversations flourished around the table, and every now and then there was an explosion of laughter. It was mostly Leila and Olive who told stories while Alan sat next to Leila, making comments about the topic and often laughing loudly. Alan's laughter was contagious. Whenever his deep baritone voice shook, everybody including Maple could not help but laugh.

Half way into the Thanksgiving feast, Maple was listening to Leila and Olive eagerly talking about the different poultry shops that they had tried in recent years when Alan winced at Maple.

"They talk a lot, don't they?"

But before Maple could reply, Leila jumped in.

"Are we being too noisy, my dear?"

"No, not at all!" answered Maple quickly. "I'm enjoying your conversations, and I'm loving this dinner party!"

"Good!" beamed Leila. "You see Maple, among us, Olive and I are the talkative ones. Alan and Robby have always been great listeners, though Robby also loved telling stories. Am I wrong, Olive?"

Olive chuckled and nodded as she took a sip from her wine glass and wiped her mouth with the napkin.

"Your husband, Robert, what was he like?" asked Maple when a moment of silence finally fell in the room as everybody's stomach became full with Olive's delicious Thanksgiving meal. The question was followed by a pause while each reflected upon their memories. It was Leila who finally opened her mouth.

"He was a true gentleman, wasn't he, Olive? Deeply kind and thoughtful," said Leila. Alan nodded, and Olive looked quietly at the orange lilies on the table. "In fact, he was the one who brought the four of us together, wasn't he? Alan and I wouldn't have married without him," said Leila.

"How is that so?" asked Maple, her curious eyes inquiring to know more about the story of these four great friends.

"Well…" Leila opened her mouth, but could not find the words. She was not used to telling a long story, but her husband was.

"Well," Alan started slowly. "Robby and I are originally from the Greater Toronto Area. We met at high school, and became really close friends. When we were finishing up high school, Robby said he wanted to try a life in a smaller town, so we both chose the Riverside College to spend the next four years of our college education. I studied English literature and Robby studied geography.

"After graduation, I stayed in Riverside and started working at a local publishing house, but Robby took a gap year and travelled across Europe just by himself. Oh, he was a big traveller by spirit, wasn't he? He did backpacking for one year, made great friends, and came back with so many interesting stories from his journey. Robby then went back to Toronto to do his master's study in education. That's when he met Emily."

He paused and sipped water from his glass before continuing. "They were classmates and great friends. Eventually, that friendship blossomed into something more. They were happily married for six years and had their first daughter Lily before we lost Emily to a horrible car accident."

Maple clasped her mouth with her hands. Everybody was quiet. Alan continued.

"That was one of the most painful moments of my entire life. To see my best friend go through such a deep grief. Lily was really the only hope Robby had at the time." Alan let out a deep sigh. "At the time, my life was quite stable in Riverside. I'd started writing books and articles alongside my job at the publishing house, and I'd also recently bought a house even though I was still single.

"One day, I told Robby to move back here to start a new life with Lily. I thought relocation could give him more space for reflection and help him to focus on his present life with Lily. Of course, I also wanted to be closer to Robby and Lily to be a better support for them. Robby agreed and temporarily moved into my house with Lily. Meanwhile, he also took a teaching job at a local high school."

"What did he teach?" asked Maple.

"Geography," answered Olive with a smile. "He loved everything that had to do with maps. He loved seeing people's life through them."

"That's also where I met Robby," said Leila. "I was teaching an art class part-time at the same high school where he was teaching. One day, he came to watch my art class, and he got really excited. You know Robby, he had a childlike nature alive in him. He could easily engage with my art class, perhaps even better than my students."

Olive and Alan both laughed.

"Anyway, we started talking and became good friends. He told me about the painful loss of Emily, and how he and Lily had recently moved to Riverside to start a new life.

"One day, Robby invited me to a dinner at his house. His landlord was his high school best friend and Robby wanted me to meet him. I was very nervous even though I was quite sure that Robby's best friend must be a good person." Leila took a breath. "Well, in the end, Robby's enthusiasm convinced me to accept the invitation. When I arrived at Robby's house, guess what? A tall and kind-looking gentleman opened the door for me with a broad smile on his face. I remember my heart racing like an arrow." Leila closed her eyes as if travelling back to the moment.

"That evening, the four of us – Robby, Lily, Alan and me – had dinner together. Alan had prepared a bean stew for all of us. Oh, how delicious it was!" Leila opened her dreamy eyes. "Two weeks later, Alan and I got married."

"Wait, what?" said Maple, her eyes widening in surprise.

"That's right," said Leila more to herself than to anybody else, holding Alan's hand. "That's how we met, honey."

Alan gently squeezed Leila's hand in recognition. After a moment of blissful silence, Alan turned to Maple.

"But the story doesn't end here, Maple. Our wedding was a very small one. For one thing, we didn't have time to prepare a big wedding, and for another, we didn't have a long list of guests to invite in the first place."

"Neither of us is from a big family," explained Leila.

"Anyway, I was looking forward to meeting my wife-to-be's best friend at our wedding because Leila had told me that her childhood best friend was going to be her bridesmaid, and I had never met her yet."

"You mean Olive?" asked Maple.

"And my best man was Robby, in case you're wondering," winced Alan.

"Wait, is that how it happened?" Maple turned to Olive, who was playing with her wine glass half amused and half embarrassed by the way the story was unfolding.

"Olive, is that how you and Robby met?"

Startled by Maple's question, Olive straightened up in her chair and cleared her throat.

"That's true, but our story is nothing dramatic like theirs. We didn't marry right away. In fact, I didn't even imagine that we would one day marry when I first met Robby." Noticing Maple's intense gaze, Olive explained.

"When we first met, Robby made it very clear to me that he wasn't thinking of remarrying any time soon, possibly ever. His grief from losing Emily was so deep that he didn't think he would ever really be ready to find a new love in his life. Of course, I understood that and I didn't inquire further." Olive paused for a second.

"Though it was strange that he even confessed it to me that night because I hadn't asked him out or anything like that. Completely out of blue, he told me that he wasn't going to remarry. If somebody else had made that comment to me during the first date, I might have felt offended. But I wasn't upset when Robby said that to me. I heard it for what it was." Olive took a sip from her glass. "I felt a deep sense of connection to Robby from the moment I first met him, something that I had never experienced before except with Leila." Olive blushed and smiled.

"Robby and I became really good friends. He and Lily would often visit me at the library where I worked on weekends. Robby was a bookworm, always looking for a new book to read. At the library, he'd first find several books for Lily's bedside stories, and then find some books for himself. After my shift, we'd often go to one of the coffee shops in Richmond and spend the late afternoon reading and chatting about each other's week."

Recalling those moments, Olive's expression softened. A few moments passed in silence. Nobody wanted to break Olive's happy memory. Then Olive continued softly.

"We had continued the ritual for about a year when Robby proposed to me and the three of us moved into this house." Olive looked around the room as if to recall that special day, and sighed. "I can't believe that more than two decades have passed since then. Those were the happiest years I ever had!" She took another sip from her glass, and turned to Maple.

"Though we looked like a family of three from outside, inside we really felt like a family of four, with Emily's presence always with us," smiled Olive. "Her presence was never haunting or binding. It was encouraging and supportive. We all felt that she was watching over our new family life. Me personally, prior to our marriage, there was a moment when I felt she had entrusted me with her precious daughter Lily."

Olive's eyes suddenly welled up with tears. Leila quickly stood up and walked around the table, gently holding Olive's shoulders. Maple looked at Olive and then at the vase of orange lilies as if to recognize Olive's pain and longing for Lily on this day of celebration.

"She entrusted me with her Lily, and what use have I been to her? Lily has now lost her father, and the only living parent she's left with is a complete wreck," sobbed Olive while Leila held her tight in her arms.

"Don't do that to yourself, Olive," said Leila gently. "Nobody thinks you're a wreck. Look at what you've done today, Olive - inviting all of us to this wonderful dinner party! Stop hurting yourself like that."

When Olive finally calmed down, she mumbled that there was a dessert in the fridge. It was a pumpkin pudding that Olive had made the night before.

"I can do that!" said Maple quickly as Olive tried to stand up. "I'll bring the pudding."

"And I'll brew the coffee," said Leila standing up. "You sit here and relax, Olive."

Maple took out the pudding from the fridge and served it in small pieces while Leila brewed four cups of coffee in Olive's old machine.

As the enticing fragrance of brewed coffee filled the room they all sat and ate pudding. The air in the room felt light again.

The remainder of the evening was calm and quiet, with each person travelling deep into their memories and thoughts, being aware of the approach of yet another end to Thanksgiving. Suddenly, Leila looked up and opened her mouth.

"Maple, we haven't yet heard about *your* family." She looked at Maple expectantly. "How are they coping with their Thanksgiving without you? They must surely miss you!"

"Oh, well..." Maple looked up with the coffee cup in her

hands. "I don't have any family here." Noticing Leila and Alan's puzzled look, Maple quickly added. "My parents currently live in Japan, and most of my relatives are on the West Coast."

"Oh, my goodness," Leila's eyes were wide open with surprise. "But you aren't from Japan, are you, Maple?"

"That's what I thought, too, Leila," said Olive laughing. "When she told me the story at Café Rose. Her mother is from Japan, but her family lived mostly in Vancouver when she was growing up."

"My parents moved to Japan when I was fifteen," smiled Maple. "I stayed on the West Coast with my grandparents for high school and college, then came to Toronto for my graduate education."

"Oh, my goodness," said Leila again. "Maple, you're not only a smart and kind lady, but you're also a great traveller!" Maple blushed at Leila's words. "Oh, Robby would have been *thrilled* to meet you, Maple. Don't you think so, Olive? A traveller meets another traveller!"

"Oh, yes, you two would have made great friends," nodded Alan.

"Do you have any siblings, Maple?" asked Leila.

"I had one twin brother, but we lost him when I was fourteen. So, I don't have any siblings now. It's just me."

The room fell silent. Maple sipped her coffee avoiding everybody's eyes. Leila quietly placed her hand on Maple's.

"I'm so sorry, Maple."

"Oh, don't be," said Maple quickly, putting a smile on her face. "It happened a long time ago."

"What happened to your brother?" asked Leila, her eyes full of concern.

"Um..." Maple paused briefly. Olive thought she saw Maple's deep blue eyes darken for a moment, and wondered how many times people might have already asked her the same question.

"It was an accident," said Maple at last. "My brother was on a trip with other students. A truck hit their bus on a highway, and the bus went off the cliff. My brother was one of the few students who didn't survive it."

Both Leila and Alan let out an audible gasp. Olive was quiet.

"I'm *so* sorry, Maple," said Leila again, squeezing Maple's hand tight. "How awful it must have been for you and your parents to lose your brother like that."

Maple smiled, but it was an awkward smile.

"Please don't cry, Leila," said Maple, looking at Leila's now watery eyes. "We are all okay now."

"Oh, Maple, after hearing about your brother," Leila said as she wiped her eyes with her napkin. "I can't imagine how much your parents must be missing you today. It must be unbearable. Look at Olive. Her daughter is in Toronto, just a train ride away, and Olive's already heartbroken as if her daughter was on the moon!"

Maple was silent. Olive badly wanted to say something to Maple, but she did not know what exactly it was that she wanted to say. She looked down at one of the decorative pumpkins in front of her and remained quiet. After a rather long silence, it was Alan who spoke at last, bringing everybody back to their senses.

"Would we like to go around the table and say what we are grateful for?"

"That's a great idea," said Leila, straightening up in her chair. "Olive, since you're the host, would you like to go first?"

Olive quickly blinked back tears and cleared her throat.

"I'm so grateful that I have been able to spend this beautiful evening with you all. My dearest friends, old and new," said

Olive, turning and smiling at Maple as she said the last word. "Who's next?"

"I'll go." Maple's clear voice rang in the quiet room. She closed her eyes and placed her hands on her chest. "I'm so grateful that I have got to meet these three wonderful people. I'll never forget about this dinner party." Then she opened her eyes. "Olive, I'm so grateful that you invited me tonight."

"Oh, you have no idea how much *we* have appreciated your presence tonight!" Leila squeezed Maple's hand once again.

"My turn," said Leila. "I'm truly grateful that I got to meet this wonderful young lady tonight. You touched my heart, Maple. You're very special. I hope that you consider us to be your family since yours live far away."

"That's so kind of you," said Maple, blushing and putting her hands together again.

"We mean it, Maple," said Alan. "We are all here for you whenever you need any help, or company, if you don't mind hanging out with old people."

"Your turn, honey." Leila elbowed her husband and Alan sat up straight on his chair.

"I'm grateful for all of the things everyone has already expressed, but I want to add one more thing - I'm grateful for Olive's delicious meal and hospitality tonight."

"That's right!" beamed Maple. "Everything was so delicious, Olive."

"Yes, my dear Olive, it was really an amazing dinner." Leila chimed in.

Bombarded by compliments, Olive's face became pink.

"Thank you, everyone. I shall take all of your words to my heart so that I can remember them when I feel low!"

The four of them stood up and worked together to clear everything away. Leila and Alan cleared the table while Maple and Olive cleaned up the kitchen. Maple arranged the dishes carried by Leila and Alan in an orderly manner before putting them in the sink for Olive to wash. Once they were washed, Maple quickly dried them with a tea towel and piled them up on the counter neatly grouping the same kind together. Olive was impressed by Maple's efficient movement, and for a moment, she wondered if this had something to do with Maple being a mathematician.

With the house returned to order, Leila, Alan, Maple and Olive all walked to the hallway to embrace the final moment of the evening.

"It was such a lovely evening, Olive," said Leila as she kissed Olive goodbye. "Thank you again for having us tonight."

"Part of me feels sad that it's over," said Olive. "I've spent my week looking forward to today."

"Oh, Olive!" Leila hugged Olive tightly.

"Olive, that flower bouquet we brought tonight," said Alan as he put on his dark red jacket. "I almost forgot to tell you. It's actually from Robby. Last night, he came to my dream and told me not to forget to bring flowers. You know how he is."

Seeing that Olive's eyes were welling with tears, Leila gently nudged Alan.

"Honey, you didn't need to make her cry again. She's had enough tears for tonight."

"They're happy tears!" protested Alan. "Olive shouldn't miss a message from Robby, you know. I'm sure you'll sleep well tonight, Olive."

Maple was standing with an amused smile, listening closely to the conversation between the three, then watched them all turn to her. Leila and Alan both gave Maple a warm hug.

"Lovely meeting you, Maple," said Leila. "Don't forget what we said tonight, my love. Think of us as your family!"

"We mean it," said Alan. Maple smiled back and wished them both a good night.

After Leila and Alan left for the evening, Olive turned to Maple.

"Thank you so much for coming tonight, Maple," said Olive sincerely. "I hope we didn't bore you."

"Bore me?" said Maple incredulously, looking at Olive, her blue eyes wide. "I had a wonderful evening with you and your fantastic friends! I was so touched by the story of you and Robby. In many ways, it was such a memorable day for me, Olive."

Olive felt a wave of warmth wash over her body, and the thing that she had been wanting to say finally escaped out of her mouth.

"I'm really sorry, Maple, about your twin brother. I had no idea. I'm so..." Olive looked for words in the air, but she could only think of one. "Shocked."

Maple gazed at Olive, trying to say something, but no words came out of her mouth.

"What was his name?" asked Olive.

"June," answered Maple. "We were both due in early June. That's why my parents named him June. I'm Maple because my mother was fond of maple trees, and thought it was a good name for a girl."

"June and Maple," said Olive quietly. "That's so lovely. They sound perfect together." Maple smiled, and Olive saw flicker of delight in Maple's dark blue eyes. "Perhaps you can tell me more about him when we meet at Café Rose next time. I would love to know more about your brother," said Olive and quickly added. "I mean, if that's something you feel okay to talk about."

"Of course, I'd love that." Maple reached for Olive and hugged her while quickly blinking away her tears. She then took out a small package from her handbag and handed it to Olive.

"Since you work at a library, I figured you like reading." Maple smiled shyly. "I have no idea if you might like this book, but I really hope you'll enjoy it."

A golden sticker with a message "Especially For You" shone on the smooth surface of the blue wrapping paper.

"Thank you, Maple," said Olive, holding the package tight against her chest. "I *do* love reading! What is it about?"

"You'll see," said Maple.

Maple hugged Olive once more at the door and stepped out of the doorway into the cool evening air. Her brown jacket shone in the darkness as she made her way to her car. Olive stood on the doorstep with her gift in hand until Maple's car disappeared from her sight.

Later that evening, Olive went upstairs in her purple nightgown with her rooibos tea and Maple's book package. Once in her bedroom, Olive curled up on the bed and placed her teacup on the nightstand. The vase of orange lilies that she had brought upstairs looked cheerful next to Olive's teacup.

Sitting on the bed with a smile, Olive took out her phone. It was past 11 pm, but she could not finish this special day without calling Lily - or at least attempting to.

The ringtone continued for a long time, but there was no answer. After anxiously waiting for a few more seconds, Olive hung up. It was disappointing not to be able to tell Lily about the beautiful Thanksgiving dinner she had just had and ask Lily how hers had been. Lily had said that she was busy with her work, but could she be working so late in the night? If Robert had been sitting next to Olive, she would have told him everything she was thinking about Lily and he would have told Olive to just relax and go to sleep, but now that was not an option either.

Olive sighed and turned her attention to Maple's gift. The golden sticker "Especially For You" caught her eye again.

Olive was excited to open the package, but wanted to savour the moment of anticipation a little longer, a habit she had had since her childhood. When there was no more reason to wait, Olive finally opened the blue wrapping paper, and a small book fell on her bed. *Take A Number: Mathematics for the Two Billion* was the title of the book.

"The Two Billion?" said Olive out loud. "What a strange title! I wonder what it means..."

As she opened the book, she found a handwritten message on the title page.

Dear Olive, the message read.

Thank you so much for inviting me to your dinner party today. This is just a small gift to celebrate our new friendship that began on a beautiful early autumn day in a cozy coffee shop. That day, we talked about perspective changes and you liked our conversation. I hope you will enjoy this book. It's written for somebody exactly like you!

Love, Maple

PS Don't be discouraged by the title! As you will see, no formulas appear in the book, it's written like a poem!

Olive stared at the message for a long time before placing the book on her nightstand. It had been a while since she received a book as a gift. The last time it was from Robert on her birthday, another Agatha Christie mystery novel. But she had never read a book whose title had the word *mathematics* in it. Leila was right. Olive had banished numbers and mathematics from her life a long time ago, and since then her life had been fine without it. Olive turned off the lamp and looked at the ceiling. *Will I be able to even read this book?* Olive's thought echoed in the quiet room.

"I guess I can at least give it a try," said Olive out loud. "Maple chose this book especially for me. Right, Robby?"

She reached her right arm in the direction of her orange lilies, touching the petals gently. Olive smiled, closed her eyes, and allowed to let herself drift off to sleep.

Chapter 4

Assumptions

The week after Thanksgiving went by rather quickly. On Tuesday, Olive had a follow-up appointment at the clinic for her injured wrist. Her patience had paid off, and her wrist was mostly recovered by now. She still needed to have a light support, but the doctor reassured her that she would be able to start using her left hand again in a week or so. On Wednesday, a new computer system was installed at Rosemary Library. It was a project that the IT department had been working on for quite a while, and the installation had finally taken place. Compared to the long preparation, the actual moment of installation was almost instantaneous, which was surprising to Olive. She and her colleagues spent the afternoon familiarizing themselves with the new system.

When Olive finished her work and came out of the library building later that afternoon, the sun had just set, and she saw the edge of the dark blue silky sky was flecked with the burning orange clouds. Mesmerized, Olive stopped and gazed at the dramatic mixture of colours. Right in front of her eyes, the bright orange light was quickly fading and merging into the sea of smooth blue evening sky.

Suddenly, Olive felt an urge to do something new and different. There was a surge of excitement in her body that she had not experienced in a while. Not knowing what exactly she was looking for, Olive stood on the sidewalk. Just then, a muffling engine sound roared on the far end of the street, and the silhouette of a bus emerged from the corner. Its two head-lights grew bigger and brighter in the darkness as it came closer.

It was not the bus that would take her home but the one she took in the morning. Without thinking, Olive crossed the street and raised her hand to signal the driver. The bus stopped, and Olive got on. It was once inside that she realized where she was wanting to go.

Olive rode all the way to the Richmond neighbourhood. Ten minutes later, Olive was standing on Main Street with an inexplicable sense of excitement. She did not have any plan. She was not going to visit Café Rose today, it was her special treat reserved for Sundays, but she was in search of something new.

Looking for inspiration, Olive started to walk. It was the oddly quiet moment between the end of afternoon and the dawn of evening. Some shops were preparing to close for the day, while restaurants and bars were gearing up for the night, with people already arriving for dinner and drinks. Olive kept walking until she arrived in front of a tiny bookshop named Orion.

The bookshop was just as small as it looked from outside. When Olive stepped in, a lady in the back counter noticed her and smiled. The place was well-lit, and the clean white walls were decorated with tiny paintings of flowers and stars. In front of Olive, there was a small shelf of stationary showing a selec-tion of notebooks. One of them had seven bright stars in the shape of a ribbon on the cover. Olive remembered Maple's journaling. Perhaps she could also try it. After caressing the seven stars on the cover, Olive decided to purchase the notebook.

When Olive finished paying at the back counter, the lady looked at Olive and asked her if she wanted to try their coffee shop as well.

"A coffee shop?" asked Olive in surprise. "Do you also have a coffee shop?"

"Yes, we do, up there."

The lady smiled and pointed to a narrow staircase leading up to a tiny attic space and a red arrow next to the staircase saying "Coffee shop this way." *How neat*, thought Olive.

"We'll be closing in about an hour, but feel free to enjoy until then." The lady smiled again and handed Olive her purchase in a paper bag.

The attic coffee shop was even tinier than the bookshop itself. But the large window facing the street and the mirrors on the wall behind made the space look more spacious than it really was. The tables, the chairs, and the floor were all wooden. The floor squeaked as Olive walked on it, which thrilled her. Olive was the only customer at this hour, and she perched herself at a small table by the window.

Just when Olive settled, the clerk came up the stairs with a small white mug in her hand. The mug had the same painting of the Orion constellation as the one on Olive's new notebook.

"There you go," said the lady placing the coffee cup on Olive's table. "It's brewed coffee. If you prefer tea, we also have a selection as well." She added quickly.

"Oh, no, coffee is perfect! I was just wondering how you manage all these by yourself. And also, where can I pay for the coffee?"

The lady smiled.

"I do have an assistant working for me during the day. But I manage the last few hours of the day by myself because the shop is usually very quiet. The coffee is on the house," she added with another smile. "We like to serve our customers some quality time to be with themselves."

And she left, leaving Olive with the wonderful smell of fresh coffee.

Olive took a sip from her cup, and opened her new notebook. She took out a pencil from her work bag, and on the first blank page, she wrote the date. Then she stared at the page for a while. It had been decades since Olive wrote her last diary entry. She took another sip of coffee and wrote:

I'm now at a tiny coffee shop called Orion. It's truly a lovely place.

She paused again, waiting for the next sentence to appear in her mind. It did not arrive for a long time. When it finally did, Olive wrote:

It's been a very strange few weeks. Many new things happened to me, and I've done many new things, too. I'm quite surprised by myself.

Olive looked out of the window and wrote:

But the best of all, I had a wonderful Thanksgiving this year.

Then she closed her notebook. She could not think of anything else to write.

Olive took out *Take A Number: Mathematics for Two Billion* from her work bag. The book had sat unread in her bag for two days in a row. Olive placed it on the table and looked at the cover. There was an illustration of a ticket machine, like the one on a bus, which led to the author's name at the bottom. Lillian Lieber. *A woman's name?* Olive was surprised. For some reason, she had assumed that the book must be written by a man since it was about numbers and mathematics. *But Maple is also a mathematician, isn't she?* thought Olive. She shook her head in disappointment at her own gender bias. Then she opened the book.

Upon turning the first few pages, Olive was relieved to discover that the book did indeed read like a poem and she felt the tension in her body melt away.

"I *can* read this!"

She smiled to herself and opened the first chapter. The title was "Why Should You Study Mathematics?" *A very good question*, thought Olive as she sipped her coffee. *Because I don't think I need to. My life is just fine without it.*

Olive skimmed through the first page. It was surprisingly easy to read, and she ended up reading every line while skimming. The author had a warm tone, and Olive liked the way she directly spoke to the reader – like a letter. One passage caught her eyes.

We shall try to tell you WHY everyone, including you, must study some Mathematics – and the more the merrier!

Olive was skeptical of this statement, but the next line intrigued her.

And, with this little book, perhaps you will even begin to like it – we hope!

Olive could not imagine herself liking math or numbers, but the thought of it was new and made her wonder what it would feel like to actually experience that feeling. She could certainly read the price tags when she did her daily shopping, and sure, she could add or subtract a few numbers in her head, but that was the extent of the relationship she had with numbers.

Lillian, the author of the book, explained to Olive that people needed to study mathematics along with science and art because it could teach us how to use our brain, which was essential for us to get along in the world. Olive recalled the distant memory of studying math at school. Did she ever learn how to use her brain through her math lessons?

"No," thought Olive. "All I learned was how to get lost and feel miserable. That's why I don't like math! It confuses my brain!"

But Olive agreed that the arts had taught her how to use her brain, especially literature. Without books, she did not know how she would have coped with her life or the world.

Just when Olive was sipping the last bit of her coffee, deep in thought, the clerk reappeared. She smiled at Olive and announced that the shop was closing soon. Olive thanked her for the coffee and left for home.

That evening after supper, Olive walked over to the cabinet in the living room where Robert used to keep his collection of CDs, pulled one out and popped it in the player. It was Brahms' piano album "10 Intermezzi" played by Glenn Gould. It had been more than a year since Olive last played it. The moment the first sound echoed, Olive was transported back to the time when she used to sit with Robert on their sofa, each with a cup of tea, savouring their quiet evening reading time. The feeling was so strong that Olive could almost sense Robert's presence in the room. Her eyes looked for the familiar figure on the sofa, and when they only found the empty spot, Olive's heart sank in disappointment.

"I'm going to read for some time, Robby," Olive called out in the empty room. "If you want to join me, you can."

Olive thought of sitting on the sofa as she used to, but then, it was strange for her to repeat the old ritual without having Robert next to her. So, she decided to sit at the dining table instead. The house had an open design, and the living room, the dining area and the kitchen all formed a single space. Olive brought her rooibos tea and Leila's Thanksgiving pumpkin biscuits from the kitchen and sat at the table with *Take A Number: Mathematics for Two Billion.* With the quiet sound of the piano from the CD player in the background, Olive started to read.

Chapter 2 was called "Mathematics Made Easy." Olive sipped her rooibos tea and took a bite from a pumpkin biscuit. The opening line was intriguing.

One of the main difficulties with the study of Mathematics by the average person has always been that they were never let in on the basic rules of the game, but was given THOUSANDS of little details to remember...

Olive was not sure if she could be counted as the average person when it came to mathematics since she was always the one who struggled most in class, but this statement resonated. From the distant memory of her math study at school, what she remembered was that there were many things to remember right from the beginning. And Olive was not good at memorizing numbers. That was the whole point of her struggle.

Now, in this little book, we shall try to show you that Mathematics is really like a game. And if you have the EQUIP-MENT and know the RULES (and you will be surprised to find how VERY FEW basic rules there are!), you can easily learn the game and even figure out your own "plays."

Olive paused for a moment to take in what she had just read. *Mathematics is like a game.* Olive had certainly never thought of it that way. *A game, like a board game or playing cards?* Olive was fond of different board games and puzzles since her childhood, and she was quite good at some of them. If mathematics was also like a game, then there might be a chance that she could actually play it well?

"Olive, is that a math book that you're reading?" Suddenly, Olive heard an amused voice next to her. "I thought you didn't like numbers."

Olive quickly turned around.

"Robby?" Her voice echoed in the empty living room. She remained motionless for a while hoping to hear more of the familiar voice that she had missed so much. But she did not hear anything. Olive looked over at the sofa on her left. Nobody was sitting there. A surge of longing washed across Olive's body. She often heard Robert's voice when she least expected it. She always wanted it to last longer, but it never did.

"Yes, Robby, I'm reading a book about math," answered Olive out loud. "I'm trying something new, you see. I thought you were the one who always wanted me to take a new adventure!" She did not hear a word in return, but felt the familiar presence around her.

"Besides, Lillian, the author of this book, tells me that math is like a game and there are only a very few rules to remember. It makes me feel that I can at least try!"

That evening, Olive sat there for a long time, even after the CD stopped playing, reading and listening. When she did not hear anything anymore, Olive finally cleared the table and went upstairs to sleep.

~

Take A Number: Mathematics for Two Billion became Olive's comfort reading. Every evening after dinner, Olive chose different music to play from Robert's CD collection and sat at the dining table with her book, rooibos tea and her evening snack. Then she would read a few chapters. It was funny that among all the books she could be reading, it was this book about numbers and mathematics that gave Olive a sense of peace and comfort. Olive liked listening to Lillian's words just like she did Maple's, and thinking about numbers pulled her head out of the daily life, out of her long list of things to blame herself about.

One night, Lillian told Olive about the transition from Arithmetic to Algebra. Both of these words were so distant to Olive that their difference did not really matter to her, but Olive was ready to be entertained by whatever Lillian was going to say.

Lillian started by recalling the kinds of numbers learned at primary school: the whole numbers, fractions, decimal fractions, and so on. She then summarized all of them in the single term *rational number*. According to Lillian, it was *any number which may be expressed as a ratio of two integers.*

As Olive read the examples of how a fraction, a decimal fraction, or even a mixed number could be seen as a ratio of two integers, she wondered why on earth they had to give different names to express the same thing in the first place. Why did she learn integers, fractions, decimal fractions as different entities at school? From the way Olive was taught, these numbers were as different as an apple and a chair. But now hearing that they could all be expressed as a ratio of two integers and captured in the single concept of rational numbers made things look a lot simpler.

After introducing negative numbers, which Olive did remember learning at middle school, Lillian said that one more difference between Arithmetic and Algebra was the usage of letters instead of numbers. This, too, Olive remembered from her secondary school. They started using a, b, c, or x, y, z in the equations instead of just numbers, and that was also when more and more formulas appeared in her textbook. Frankly speaking, Olive had never understood the point of introducing these letters in mathemtics. It was strange for her to see letters mixed among numbers, and she never understood how to treat them properly. But Lillian said something curious:

Another advantage of the use of letters is that, in solving a problem, you can do it more easily and more directly, because you may use a letter to stand for a quantity which is unknown, and still go ahead and work with it, ...

What on earth does this mean? Olive wondered. Perhaps this was something she could ask Maple about when she would see her this coming Sunday. In fact, Olive had so many things to tell Maple about her week that she could not wait for her next visit to Café Rose.

When Sunday finally arrived, Olive left for Richmond earlier than usual. In order to control her excitement, she got off the bus two stops before the one for Café Rose, and walked down Main Street enjoying the crisp autumn air on her face and the presence of people who passed by her. It had only been a month since the day Olive had a panic attack on the street and sought refuge at Café Rose, but the day felt like a very long time ago for Olive. As she swiftly walked through the crowd in her emerald green autumn jacket, Olive looked into the glass windows of the shopfronts, many of which now had Halloween display, some cute, others spooky.

Café Rose was still bustling with people from lunchtime when Olive arrived. To her disappointment, Maple was not there. An elderly gentleman was occupying Maple's regular corner seat at the counter. Feeling disturbed, Olive made her way to her usual seat by the window and ordered her cappuccino and croissant.

What if she won't come today? A thought crossed Olive's mind as she settled into her seat and gazed out of the window. But even if Maple were not to come, Olive still had important rituals to perform. When the waitress came back to Olive with her cappuccino and croissant, Olive took out her diary, and opened a new page. Sipping her cappuccino, she started to write.

It's Sunday afternoon at Café Rose. My favourite time of the week. I feel I've waited for this moment for so long! But I'm a little disappointed because Maple isn't here today.

She stopped and looked out of the window. Some yellow leaves fell from the nearby tree and danced gently in the air before resting on the ground.

There were many things I wanted to tell her about, ask her about. It saddens me not to see her.

Olive stared at her diary. It had only been a few days since she started writing in her diary, but words were already flowing more naturally, and Olive was surprised by the sense of comfort it brought to her. Writing in her diary was like telling her stories to a dearest friend who would listen to her whenever and whatever she had to say.

Suddenly, Olive felt that her diary should have a name. She

looked at the pale blue diary cover with seven shiny dots in the shape of the Orion constellation. A smile dawned on Olive's face.

"Orion, your name is Orion." As she said it, the name sounded just perfect and the smile on Olive's face became even wider. Olive continued.

Now that you have a name, Orion, I feel invited to tell you more of my story. The biggest news I wanted to share is that I have started reading a new book called Take A Number: Mathematics for Two Billion. *It's a gift I got from Maple on Thanksgiving.*

Taking a small bite from her croissant, she continued.

At first, I wasn't sure if I could read this book because it's about numbers and math. I banished numbers and math from my life a long time ago because, you know, I never got along well with them. But the truth is, this book is giving me comfort. Comfort. Can you believe that?

She paused and sipped her cappuccino.

I also resumed my evening reading time in the living room. I hadn't done that since Robby passed away. I guess I was afraid that I would miss him too much if I did.

Olive looked out of the window, carefully thinking back on that evening.

I even played the music from Robby's CD collection. And I felt his presence.

Olive stopped, holding her pencil tight, searching for words.

I don't know, it was such a strong feeling... I felt his presence right beside me. Once, I even heard him speak to me. He teased me about the book!

Olive stared at the page for a second. Then she felt a tightening in her throat.

I wish he were here. I wish I could discuss the book with Robby.

Her eyes burned as she scribbled the last sentence. Olive looked up quickly so that the tears returned to her eyes, but one drop travelled down her cheek and fell on her diary page, making the very first watermark on her writing.

"Hi Olive!" A cheerful voice rang behind her. Quickly wiping away her eyes, Olive turned around. Maple was standing next to her holding the straps of her green backpack. Her soft chestnut hair was dancing beneath the orange, hand-woven head warmer. Olive felt her heart leap with joy.

"Maple!" As Olive embraced Maple, the crisp outdoor smell tingled her nose. Maple must have been walking outside for a while. "So happy to see you."

"Me too, Olive," said Maple. "I'm glad I made it in time. I came running, I didn't want to miss you."

Maple told Olive that she had been marking midterm exams for one of her classes this week, and that was the reason why she was late.

"Which class?" asked Olive as she watched Maple slide herself into her regular spot on the left corner. The elderly gentleman must have left some time ago. Olive was glad that Maple did not have to sit anywhere else.

"Linear algebra," answered Maple, storing her bag under the seat.

"Linear algebra?"

The word sounded very technical, but Olive recognized a familiar word.

"Maple, is that something related to algebra?"

"Yes, it is!" Maple quickly turned to Olive, her eyebrows slightly raised with surprise. "Linear algebra is a particular branch of algebra. Did you study it before, Olive?"

"No," Olive quickly shook her head, then added. "Not that I remember, at least. But I'm curious to learn about it."

Seeing the clear surprise on Maple's face, Olive blushed. She took a deep breath and smiled at her.

"I'm really enjoying the book you gave me."

"Oh!" Maple's surprise quickly turned into delight. Her face now shone with excitement. "Are you reading it already? Do you really like it?"

Olive told Maple how she was first afraid that she would not be able to understand the book because the title contained two things that she had avoided her entire adult life: numbers and mathematics. But then she was surprised about the poem-like format of the book and the encouraging tone of the author.

"I really thought that the book was going to be full of numbers and formulas and things that I cannot comprehend. That's pretty much my experience with math. I really, really struggled with math at school, and I felt unwelcome to the subject." Olive shared, sipping her cappuccino. "But this book is different. I *can* understand what the author is telling me. I *can* follow her thoughts on the page even though she's talking about numbers and math!"

Maple nodded, carefully listening and watching the excitement on Olive's face.

"There was one more thing that shocked me - in a good way," Olive carefully added as she turned to Maple. "When I first saw the title, I assumed a strict male voice would be behind the book. But the book is actually written by a woman author. And she has such a friendly and encouraging voice." Olive sipped her cappuccino. "I guess all I'm trying to say here is that this book really caught me by surprise. It broke off a few assumptions that I was having about numbers and math. It feels good to know that I can read and learn *something* about numbers and math."

Maple dropped her gaze, thinking. When she opened her mouth, her voice was low as if to cherish a precious thought.

"Assumptions are tricky, aren't they?" said Maple, sipping her coffee and gazing out of the window. "Because most of the time they're invisible. We're so used to our assumptions that we don't even realize that they're there." Maple looked at her coffee.

"But our actions are based on our assumptions. For example, when I come to this café, I assume that I can have a coffee. I also assume that the café stands at the same spot each time I come. So, I don't even think twice about these things before I leave home each Sunday." Maple looked at Olive. "I don't know what I would do without any assumptions about anything, do you? That would be awfully confusing. To try to spend a day without assuming anything at all! So, assumptions are useful in that way." Maple held her coffee cup gently. "But nonetheless, it's liberating to be aware of at least some of our assumptions," said Maple and smiled.

Olive sipped her cappuccino quietly. The thought was new to her. Olive had never consciously considered the fact that she was carrying around assumptions, nor of the content of those assumptions. Like Maple said, they were always invisible to Olive. She also realized with amazement how an observation like this had the power to make her experiences more insightful and interesting.

Olive looked at her own reflection in the window, and wondered when was the last time she made a new friend, not just any friend but a friend with whom she could sit and talk about life like this. Robert? But that was decades ago. The familiar silhouette of the middle-aged woman in the glass looked happier and more lively than the one she remembered. *Trying new things*, thought Olive. A corner of her mouth lifted with a smile.

When they finished talking about the book, a brief silence fell between them.

"Have you talked with Lily since Thanksgiving, Olive?" asked Maple. From her clear and determined voice, it felt as if she had been meaning to ask this question for a long time. Olive shook her head.

"I tried calling her right after our Thanksgiving dinner, but she didn't answer. And I haven't called her since." Olive sighed. "I really want to talk to her, but whenever I pick up the phone and try to dial her number, I feel strongly that I shouldn't."

"Why?" asked Maple with a puzzled look. Olive sighed again, her right hand caressing the edge of the saucer restlessly.

"I really don't know her situation right now. What she's doing, if she's well, if she has any problems with anything..."

"That's why you want to call her, right? To ask her how she is?"

Olive looked down at her empty cup, and said, "I'm afraid that she may not want to talk to me." There was a pause.

"Why do you think that?"

"I feel I've failed her as a mother, Maple," said Olive, without moving her eyes from the cup. "A mother should be present when her daughter needs help, but I wasn't present for her."

Maple was quiet. Olive took a deep breath and continued.

"For months after my husband passed away, I was completely paralyzed, completely at a loss. I had a hard time putting things together even for myself. To be honest, I don't really remember those days clearly. My mind was constantly blurred, you know."

Maple nodded.

"I didn't feel like cooking, I didn't feel like cleaning the house, I didn't feel like doing anything. Thankfully, I continued my work at the library, and at least when I was out, I seemed to be functioning. But once at home, I was paralyzed. When Lily came back home for last Christmas, I was still in that state. Lily was also very quiet throughout the visit. I tried to sit and talk with her, but she always made herself busy cooking and cleaning the house instead."

Olive took a sip from her water glass.

"That was the first time I felt she didn't want to talk to me. And after Christmas, whenever I tried to reach her by phone, she didn't pick the call. She would text me back, but she would rarely talk to me."

Maple was still quiet. Olive let out a deep sigh and turned to Maple, where she was found deeply immersed in Olive's words, every inch of her face showing the compassion she felt for Olive's pain. Olive suddenly worried if her long confession had burdened Maple.

"I'm sorry, Maple. I know you didn't come here to listen to an old woman's problem."

Looking for a change of topic, Olive decided to ask the question she had always wondered ever since she learned about Maple's family in Japan.

"So, how often do you see your family, Maple? Do they come here to visit you, or do you go to Japan to see them?"

Maple was startled to find a question suddenly directed to her. She reached for her pain au chocolat and took a bite before answering.

"Once a year, I guess. I'm the one who usually travels, not my parents."

Olive looked at Maple in amazement. Only once a year? It had been less than a year since Olive last saw Lily, and it was getting unbearable.

"How about phone calls? Do you get to talk to your parents quite often?" asked Olive.

"Once or twice a month, I guess," answered Maple.

"Don't you miss them?"

"Not really," said Maple, then added quickly. "I mean, we don't have much to talk about. They are quite busy with their own lives."

Olive had never met a young woman who was as independent as Maple. Everything Olive heard from Maple felt like news from another world.

"Listening to you, Maple," said Olive after a long pause, "makes me feel small for being disturbed by not talking to my daughter often. I know Lily has her own life." Olive sighed. "And I know that she's more than capable of navigating her life, just like you. But there's part of me that wants to feel connected to her. I want to be in touch."

Her voice came out strong in the last sentence, surprising Olive herself.

"Olive," Maple's clear voice rang in Olive's ears. "If you were my mother, I'd be thrilled to receive your calls. Talking with you is so much fun and it lights me up."

Olive turned to Maple. Maple had just finished eating her pain au chocolat and she was sipping her coffee.

"I'd be even happier if you could visit me sometimes."

"Really?" Olive leaned forward.

"Yes, a mother's visit is always special, you know."

Olive wondered what special visit Maple might have received from her mother, but her thought was interrupted when the waitress came to them with a mop in her hand and said that the café was closing.

"We are the last ones again!" said Olive loudly as she stood up and picked up her jacket.

"Yes, we are!" Maple chimed in with a smile as the waitress started to clear the table.

The waitress laughed with Maple and Olive before removing her apron and disappearing in the back.

"Will you be here again next Sunday?" asked Olive as they stepped out of the bakery onto Main Street. The sun was hanging on the horizon and dusk was fast approaching from the other side of the sky.

"Well, next week, I will probably miss it," Maple answered as she put her hands in the pockets of her shiny brown jacket. "I'll be travelling to Toronto next weekend to attend a workshop."

"Oh," said Olive trying to hide her slight disappointment at the prospect of not seeing Maple the following weekend. "Is that something related to your work, Maple?"

"Yes, something like that," said Maple with a smile. "I'll be presenting a talk at the research workshop. Once in a while I do that to keep up with the world."

Olive was again impressed by Maple's aspiring spirit and felt shaken up.

"Well, I wish you good luck on that. I'm sure you'll do a great job at the presentation."

"Thank you, Olive, hearing that from you is such an encouragement."

After parting with Maple, Olive walked to her bus stop, feeling light and happy thinking back on their conversation at Café Rose. One piece in particular kept replaying in her head. *If you were my mother, I'd be thrilled to receive your calls. I'd be even happier if you could visit me sometimes.* Could that be true? wondered Olive. Was there a chance that Lily might actually be feeling that way about Olive?

There was a loud engine sound in front of her and Olive saw her bus arriving. It was only when Olive got onto the bus with other passengers and settled on a seat that Olive realized that she had completely forgot to ask Maple about her question about algebra.

Chapter 5

Definitions

October was wrapping up quickly as it always did. The little rain storm which hit the town a few days previously had ripped away most of the leaves remaining on the trees, and the streets were now filled with patches of different coloured leaves. "The final moment of beauty before the long silence" was how Olive would call this time of year. Soon the first layer of snow would arrive and hide everything under a white blanket.

The more leaves fell from the trees, the more people visited Rosemary Library. After many outdoor adventures of summer, autumn seemed to be the season when people had an increased appetite for reading. Being in charge of the children's books, Olive talked daily with young children and their guardians to help them find the books they wanted.

One day, a little girl of about six years old came to Olive with her younger brother. Olive was organizing a bookshelf when she felt a pull on her apron.

"My brother is looking for a book about the moon," the girl told Olive in a small but determined voice.

"A book about the moon?" Olive knelt down, scanning her memory for all the books she knew were about the moon. "What do you like about the moon, my dear?"

Upon hearing Olive's question, the little boy was excited to tell Olive about the big, round moon he had seen the night before with his mother. Olive remembered that this month's full moon was approaching soon. When Lily was small, Olive would often take her out on an evening walk to watch the full moon together. A smile broke across Olive's face.

Olive took the two children to another bookshelf and handed them the book *Papa, Please Get the Moon for Me* by Eric Carle. Olive opened the book and read the title for them, and showed them the pictures of the moon inside. They seemed happy and immediately loved the book. The girl thanked Olive on behalf of her brother, and they left.

Once they were gone, Olive turned back to the shelf she was organizing. But a piece of paper caught her attention on the reading table in front of her. Somebody must have left their book titles, thought Olive. She leaned over it to check what was written there.

"Suppose you are standing at the centre of a circle on the ground. How can you go outside of this circle without stepping over the circle?"

Olive read it twice before she was able to register what she had just read. This was not a book title, but instead sounded like a puzzle. Olive looked around to see if anybody was looking for this piece of paper. When she saw nobody, she slipped the note into her pocket. Somehow, she felt compelled to keep it.

Olive forgot about this whole event for the rest of the afternoon. It was when she finished her work and was waiting for her bus that the mysterious question suddenly came back to her mind again.

Right in front of her, there was a manhole covered by a round lid. Olive stood on the lid, and thought how on earth she could go outside of the circle without stepping over the border. *That's not possible, is it?* thought Olive to herself. From where she stood, if she wanted to go outside of the lid, she certainly had to cross the border at least once. There was no way she could step out of this manhole lid without stepping over its circle-shaped boundary. Olive kept stepping in and out wondering and wondering how on earth it was possible to do what she was doing without crossing the circle boundary until finally her bus route for home arrived and picked her up.

On Friday, Olive had her regular meetup with Leila in the Willow Park. For years, Friday late afternoons were when Olive and Leila cherished their quality time together and caught up on each other's week. Their meeting place changed depending on the season and their mood of the day, but their favourites included a selection of local coffee shops and the Willow Park near the river. Especially during summer, when the weather was nice, Olive and Leila would often meet in the park after their work, sitting under one of the willows by the water and exchanging stories from each other's week. Though autumn was nearing the end and it was now too cold for them to sit on a bench, Olive suggested Leila to meet in the Willow Park and take a walk to enjoy the final autumn beauty together.

When Olive arrived in the park, Leila was standing under their favourite willow looking at the waves on the river surface. Her face broke into a smile as soon as she saw Olive, and she jumped with excitement when she noticed that Olive was no longer wearing a support on her arm.

"Oh, Olive, finally your arm is free again!" exclaimed Leila, catching Olive tightly in her arms. "Now that your wrist is recovered, I don't have to worry about squashing your hand anymore!"

Olive laughed, and the two of them started to walk along the river. The bright afternoon sunlight shone on their faces, warming their skin. Leila told Olive about her new illustration project.

"Alan is working on a new story about friendship," explained Leila, unable to contain her excitement. "And he wants to base it on the actual story of *our* friendship."

"Really?" laughed Olive.

"Oh, it's not a joke, Olive. Alan really wants to write about us because this year is the 50th anniversary of our friendship!" Leila's eyes started to shine like Lake Louise on a sunny summer day. Olive stopped in the middle of her step.

"Oh, no, Leila, I don't think it's a good idea to write a story about *us*!" She looked down at the tips of her toes, then turned to Leila. "First of all, it's not going to attract young children. And second of all," Olive took a deep breath. "It makes me feel *old*, and I don't like that!"

There was a pause. A wind blew by them and a flock of geese called high above in the sky.

"Listen, Olive," said Leila, gently holding Olive's hand and starting to walk again. "He's not going to write a story about 56 year old ladies. He'll write about us when we were young, when we were little girls! Now, that's certainly appealing to young children."

When Olive tried to protest further, Leila raised her hand and continued.

"And Olive, it's a *fact* that we're 56 years old, and it's our *choice* to perceive it as young or old. *I think 50th anniversary is an amazing accomplishment for a friendship, and I want to celebrate it properly!*"

From the way Leila was emphasizing certain words, Olive realized that she had greatly disappointed her friend. Extra emphasis had always been Leila's way of hiding her embarrassment ever since they first became friends in primary school.

"I'm sorry Leila, I didn't mean to spoil your excitement," Olive apologized. "You're right, there is no reason why I should feel so negative about my age." Olive held Leila's hand tight over two layers of gloves and smiled at her. "And I completely agree that the 50th anniversary of our friendship requires a proper celebration."

Since Leila was quiet for a while, Olive thought of something to talk about, and remembered the mysterious question she found at the library the other day.

"Leila, what do you think of this question?" started Olive. "Suppose you're standing at the centre of a circle. How would you go outside of this circle *without* stepping over the circle?" Leila looked startled and stopped, but Olive continued.

"For example, right now, I'm standing at the centre of a circle." Olive picked up a twig and drew a circle on the ground so that she was located at its centre spot. "That is, I'm located inside of this circle, see? Now, how can I stand outside of this circle – like you do, Leila – without stepping over this circle?"

Olive looked at Leila ready to hear her thoughts, but Leila was speechless. After an awkward silence, Leila carefully examined Olive's face.

"So, you started working on a math problem?"

"What? A math problem?"

Olive blinked her eyes in surprise.

"Yes, Olive, what you just said sounds like a math problem, doesn't it?"

Olive looked down at the twig in her hand and the circle drawn on the ground. The situation reminded Olive more of her childhood than a math problem and made her chuckle. Olive turned back to Leila.

"Oh, come on, Leila. This is just a little puzzle I found at my library the other day!" Olive waved the twig around. "I don't think it's anything math-related, except maybe the circle! Plus, what's wrong if it *is* math-related?"

Then Olive quickly shut her mouth. She had not yet told Leila about the new book she was reading and that she was now learning a bit of mathematics from it.

"Anyway, it's just a puzzle, Leila. There's nothing to worry about. You know I love puzzles," Olive concluded and cleared her throat. "Now, tell me, Leila, what do you think? How can I go out of this circle without stepping over the circle itself?"

"Well..." started Leila, coming back to her senses and compelled to say something under Olive's enthusiasm. "Well, I suppose such a thing isn't possible."

"Why do you think that?" asked Olive. Leila looked at Olive and the circle around her feet.

"Do you think it's possible? To stand outside of the circle from where you are now, without stepping over the circle itself?"

"No, I don't," said Olive. "But I'm wondering *why* we think that way. I mean, why do we think that it's not possible? Can we explain the reason?"

Leila paused for a second, trying to understand what Olive had just said.

"You want to know *why* we think that it's not possible for a person inside a circle to come out of it without stepping over the circle?"

"That's right," Olive nodded.

"That's pretty obvious, isn't it? Try to come out of the

circle, Olive," said Leila. Olive stepped over the circle and stood outside of it.

"I'm now outside!"

"Yes, but you've crossed over the circle," said Leila.

"I have," said Olive.

"Can you do it again but without stepping over the circle?"

Olive went back inside.

"Here we go," said Olive and stepped out of the circle, this time from the other side.

"You've stepped over the circle again!" said Leila.

"You see, Leila," said Olive. "I can do this a thousand times, but I can assure you that I will always have to step over this circle if I want to stand outside of it."

"How so?" asked Leila, intrigued. Though it seemed obvious, she could not think of any logical explanation.

"Because the situation doesn't change if I choose this direction or that direction. Whichever direction I choose, I'm always dealing with a piece of the same circle in front of me. This whole thing is about me moving from inside of the circle to outside of it. And in order to achieve that," Olive pointed at the circle. "I must cross a piece of this circle. Therefore, it's not possible for me to come out of this circle without crossing over the circle itself."

The two of them stared at the circle for a while. Then Leila abruptly opened her mouth.

"But what if you stood still, and the circle moved instead?" Leila flinched upon finishing the sentence as if to regret expressing her thought, which sounded quite lame. But Olive was excited.

"I haven't thought of that, Leila. Yes, why do I always have to move?" said Olive. "We can imagine that this circle is made out of a rubber band or something. I stand inside the circle and we move the circle around instead of me moving!"

Leila blushed. She was not used to having her thoughts appreciated like this, not even in the 50 years of friendship with her best friend.

"Leila, you've just given me a new way to think about this question! It might give us a way to come out of the circle without crossing over the circle," beamed Olive.

The two of them started to walk again. The sky was turning orange, and the late afternoon wind gently pushed the fallen leaves to travel along the path. Olive and Leila listened to the rustling sound of the leaves wordlessly as they walked. It was one of those moments when silence created more intimacy between them than words.

After a long silence, Olive looked up at the sky and opened her mouth.

"Leila, I've been thinking about Lily. You know, it's been really a long time since I last spoke with her properly."

Leila nodded quietly, listening.

"Actually, I tried calling her after our Thanksgiving dinner."

"And?"

"She didn't pick up the call again," said Olive and sighed. "We've never been like this before, Lily and I. We used to call each other every week! This is the first time we've been out of touch for so long, and it's tearing me apart."

Leila walked beside Olive without a word.

"It may sound strange, but since Robby passed away last year, I feel like I've lost Lily, too." Looking over the river, Olive continued. "I know I disappointed her when she came home last Christmas. I wasn't functioning well at all, I was buried in my own grief. Lily must have been coping with a lot herself, and it pains me to think that I wasn't present to be of help to her." Olive bit her lip. "But the truth is, Leila, I miss her awfully. I want to see her."

They had come to the end of the park area. The foot path continued further into the woods, but Olive and Leila stopped and stood by the water looking over the other shore.

"Maple said I could visit Lily instead of waiting for her."

"And?"

"But I'm afraid that Lily may not want to talk to me anymore."

Olive's eyes followed a flock of geese moving in the water far away. Leila took a deep breath and turned to Olive.

"Olive, Lily loves you. She *adores* you. You know that."

"But that was when Robby was still alive," blurted Olive, surprised by the defensive tone of her own voice.

"And what difference does that make?" Leila pushed further. "How is that relevant? Why does Lily have to stop loving you because Robby has gone?"

Olive felt a stinging pain in her chest. Suddenly, it was as if she had been walking on a high mountain. The air became thin, and Olive tried to catch her breath.

"Because I'm so incapable without him!" cried Olive. The sudden overflow of emotions consumed Olive like a tsunami. "I'm not strong, Leila. I'm not capable. All I've done since that day is to pretend. Acting as if I can manage things, as if I'm functioning like before. But I'm not fine at all!"

Olive was now sobbing.

"Lily feels all this. This is *not* the mother she knew. This is *not* the mother she wants."

Leila stood motionless, her wet eyes mirroring every inch of pain revealed in each word Olive spoke.

"When I'm alone at home, I miss Robby. And I start thinking about all the things I've done wrong for our Lily since he left."

Olive could not speak anymore. Her suppressed sob echoed

around them. With one swift move, Leila stepped towards Olive and pulled her shaking body into her arms.

"Oh, Olive," whispered Leila, holding her friend tight in her arms. "Oh, Olive. Stop being harsh on yourself. You know how much Robby loves you. He would be heartbroken to see you blaming yourself like that. He's already sad that he had to leave you and Lily behind."

Olive breathed heavily into Leila's shoulder. Now tears streamed down her cheeks. Gently patting Olive's back, Leila continued.

"For Robby's sake, stop being harsh on yourself, Olive. And let's think about how you can connect with Lily again. I'm sure Lily wants to see you, too. What if she just didn't know how to talk with you after what happened? When we have much to say, it can actually become harder to speak, you know."

Olive took a deep breath and wiped away her tears. Her breath had become more even now. Olive wondered when the last time was that she had cried like this in her friend's arms. Even after Robert's death, Olive had not revealed her emotions to Leila despite their close friendship. She had feared that what she carried inside was too complicated to share and did not want to overwhelm her dear friend with her emotions. But now, being embraced in Leila's arms, Olive felt her friend's strength. Her emotions poured out, but nothing collapsed. Olive and Leila both watched the pain quietly flow away like the water in the river and a sense of peace returned to the air.

Olive invited Leila for dinner that evening since Alan was away on a business trip to Toronto. They prepared a tomato stew together and chatted for some more time over dinner about their work, their new cooking recipes, and gossiped about their mutual friends. Olive played Oscar Peterson's jazz piano collection on the CD player when it was time for dessert and tea. As the first note of the music came from the player, Leila looked up.

"It feels as if Robby were still here," said Leila in a distant voice. Olive smiled, and the two of them sat in peaceful silence, sipping their rooibos tea and taking bites from Olive's lemon cake.

After Leila left, Olive cleared the kitchen, and thought she would like nothing more than to take a relaxing bath after the long week. Olive went to the bathroom upstairs and ran the hot water in the bathtub. Since the outside temperature was quickly dropping, she wanted to make sure that the water was hot enough so that her body could relax better. She also sprinkled some Himalayan bath salts from an old box she found on the shelf, which had been her birthday gift from Lily a few years ago.

Once the water was ready and Olive settled in the bathtub warm and cozy however, the least expected thing happened. That mysterious question about a circle came back to Olive's mind as if it had been waiting for her sole attention. Olive was not sure if this question was the best company for her evening relaxation, but she accepted the visit anyway since it was not going to be as painful as spending her thoughts on self-doubts and self-blames.

"So, where was I?" said Olive. There were a few hair ties on the edge of the sink. Olive picked one and placed it on the water in front of her. Now the water surface represented the ground, and the hair tie was the circle on the ground. Olive placed her index finger in the middle of the hair tie to represent the person standing inside the circle.

"Okay, so how can I make it so that my finger will be outside of this circle but without crossing over the circle?" Olive remembered Leila's earlier comment, and kept her finger fixed in one place and moved the hair tie instead. She first moved the hair tie horizontally on the water. But of course, the hair tie could not move past her finger.

"Inside and outside..." murmured Olive. *Right now, my finger is inside of the circle. In order to go outside, it has to cross the border, which is this hair tie. So, it's inevitable that my finger crosses it at one point.*

"I mean, that's what a border is, isn't it?" said Olive out loud. Her voice echoed in the bathroom. "A border is a separation between inside and outside, isn't it? Like a border between two countries?"

Olive moved the hair tie around her finger.

"So, if I were to move from one side of the border to the other, by the very meaning of it, I must cross the border somewhere. Unless..." said Olive, and moved the hair tie upward, away from the water, and then landed it next to her finger so that her finger was now located outside of the circle. "I do this. But this is cheating, isn't it? Once I bring this hair tie outside of the water, it's not clear what the *inside* of this hair tie means..."

Olive started to feel very hot. She might have run the water too hot tonight. Or it could have been the effect of the Himalayan bath salts. In any case, Olive was steaming and she could no longer think clearly. She stood up. Now it was time for her to really rest.

Wearing her purple nightgown, Olive walked along the corridor barefoot. The cool touch of the wooden floor was welcome relief. Just before reaching the bedroom, Olive always passed by Robert's room, which was a large room that he used to use as his home office. Olive had not changed anything in the room since the day he died, and every week she took the time to clean the room properly. She felt it would keep her husband's presence better that way. Usually, the door was closed, but tonight it was left ajar. Olive reached for the doorknob thinking of closing it, but then she changed her mind. She pushed the door wide open and stepped inside.

The moment her feet felt the soft carpet and her nose inhaled the smell of books, Olive immediately felt calm and grounded as she had used to in the presence of Robert. The yellow light from the corridor and the street lights coming in from the window were sufficient for Olive to recognize the objects in the room.

To her left, there was a wall of book shelves full of old and new books that Robert had collected since he was a student. On her right, there was a collection of familiar pictures on the wall that Robert had taken during his solo trips in Europe. And in the back wall next to the window hung a colourful portrait of Robert and Olive drawn by Lily when she was in kindergarten. Two big faces with big eyes and big smiles drawn in crayons were beaming as if they were about to jump out of the frame.

Olive made her way toward the window and stopped in front of the desk. On it was a small globe that Robert used to treasure. It was Olive's favourite, too. When Robert was alive, they would often spend hours looking at this globe together, talking about different countries and regions and people's different lifestyles. Even though Olive was not comfortable travelling in real life, she enjoyed making an imaginary trip with Robert around the world. By looking at different countries on the globe, Olive would ask Robert what he knew about the place and ask him to tell her the stories so that they could feel as if they were travelling there together.

Tonight, the globe was shining quietly in the silver street lights from the window. As Olive gently touched the globe, she noticed that there was a rubber band misplaced right underneath it. It was one of those super rubber bands that could bear more force than the normal ones.

Olive picked it up, and without much thought, placed it on

the globe. When she leaned in, she saw the dot "Toronto" located right inside of the loop created by the rubber band. Out of her playful habit, Olive stretched the rubber band and made the loop bigger. Doing this on a globe was more fun than doing it on a flat table surface. She stretched more and more, trying to see how big the loop could become. Soon it contained the whole of North America, and then the entire American Continent.

The rubber band seemed to be elastic enough to even stretch further and hug the entire circumference, but Olive did not want to risk damaging the globe just in case the rubber band broke while it was stretching. So, she stopped. However, in her imagination, the rubber band continued to stretch and finally became large enough to hug the entire circumference of the globe. After that, it started to shrink, but this time on the "other side" of the globe covering the Eurasian Continent. Finally, the loop became as small as its original size and settled somewhere on Australia - the antipodal point of Toronto. That was what had happened in her imagination.

Olive placed the rubber band upon Australia, and compared it with the location where the journey started. When she followed the track back to Toronto with her finger, Olive realized that something most unusual had just happened. The dot "Toronto" on the globe, which used to be located inside of the rubber band, was now located outside of it.

She brought the rubber band back to Toronto. She needed to follow the procedure again. In her imagination, Olive started to stretch the rubber band and made the loop bigger and bigger. The loop contained larger and larger area of the American Continent and its surrounding oceans and finally contained exactly half of the earth surface when it hugged the circumference of the globe. Then the loop started to shrink on the *other side* of the globe, now containing the Eurasian Continent and all the South Eastern Asian countries. Finally, the loop was back to its original size and settled on Australia, which was exactly the *opposite* location from Toronto on the globe. The amazing thing about this procedure was that Toronto seemed to have moved outside of the loop without ever crossing the loop itself.

"How on earth did Toronto move from inside to outside of the loop without crossing the rubber band?" According to Olive's understanding of what a border was, such a thing should not be possible. There should be no way a dot could move from one side to the other side of the border without physically crossing it.

"Oh, boy," said Olive. "What on earth is happening here?"

It was not a very pleasant feeling to go to bed with an unresolved question, but she had no choice tonight. She was too tired to think anything anymore. Olive closed the curtains and left the room.

"Good night, Robby," said Olive and kissed the air as she closed the door. "I'm curious to know what you think of this mysterious question. But please wait until tomorrow. Let me be free from it while I sleep."

Chapter 6

Maple

The second floor corridor of the Fields Institute was lively at this hour of the day. Even though it was Saturday, with two workshops happening in parallel, quite a few people were sitting and talking over hot drinks and snacks during afternoon break time.

Half hidden in the echoing voices of people, Maple stood in the corridor all by herself, quietly staring at the helix staircase that vertically spiralled through the building from the ground floor to the top. She had just given a short presentation on her research in the early afternoon teatime session. As soon as she finished, she came out in order to catch a breath and centre herself before going back to the seminar room for the last talk of the day.

Five hours had passed since the workshop had started, and Maple was feeling weary. It was her usual reaction to most mathematics workshops and conferences that she attended. She was aware that this peculiar sense of fatigue and emptiness in her body was not the consequence of her effort to understand the complicated mathematical talks but of her inability to connect with the environment around her. She always felt at odds with the atmosphere, as if part of her was estranged.

As Maple gazed at the helix staircase and thought back on the past few hours, she saw a person who seemed to be of a similar age to her walking up the staircase. *He reminds me of June,* thought Maple. *Had he been alive, would he also have been attending this workshop?* Though Maple knew June's dream was to become a medical doctor and not a mathematician, somewhere in her mind, she could not help fantasizing about doing everything she was doing now with her twin brother.

It was a few weeks before the accident. When Maple came back from school one day, she found a book titled *History of Geometry* on the family dining table. June must have left it there since nobody else in the house would read such a book. Usually, Maple would ignore any of June's math books, but that day, something invited her to take a look. As she sat down with a jam and butter toast that she had made herself for a snack, Maple opened the book and flipped through the first few pages.

At the beginning, there was a page with four biscuits of different shapes. One big circle, one small circle, one square, and one ellipse. Then there was a question written underneath it: *Which of these shapes are different?*

Who would ask such an obvious question? thought Maple. *Of course, they are all different except for the two circles!*

As she continued reading, however, the author said that there were different ways in which we could answer this question. We could say that these four shapes were all different because none of these were identical to each other. We could also say that only the two circles were of the same shape and the rest were different because they had different names. Another way to look at them was to say that only the square was of a different shape because the other three shapes could be obtained by observing a circle from different angles. Then finally, we could even say that the four shapes were all the same because they could be seen as some sort of deformation of a circle by imagining that they were made of rubber bands.

"What kind of nonsense is this?" said Maple out loud. *But it's interesting,* echoed another voice in her head. *It's interesting that there are different ways to distinguish between these four shapes.*

When she finished her snack, Maple brought the book to her room. She laid down on her bed, and instead of opening Phillip Pullman's *The Golden Compass*, which she had recently been immersed in, Maple turned the page of *History of Geometry*. At first, she was just going to read a few pages. But a few pages turned into a dozen, and into a few chapters. Without realizing it, Maple spent the whole afternoon reading the book.

Maple realized how much time had elapsed when she heard a knock on the door and saw the clock on her desk. It was 6 pm. Soon it would be supper time. There was another knock. Her room door was left ajar, and she saw June's face peeking from the gap.

"June!" shouted Maple and sat up on her bed. "You scared me!"

"Sorry," said June, pushing the door wide open and entering the room. "Didn't mean to. I just wanted to ask you if you saw my book, *History of Geometry* by any chance. This morning, I left it on the dining table, but it's not there anymore. I'm looking for it."

"Well, it's here!" said Maple, holding the book in front of

her. "I found it on the table while I was having my snack, and I thought about taking a look at it."

"Are you reading it?" June's voice raised in surprise.

"Well, I was just having a look," said Maple quickly, pretending to be unaware of June's curious gaze. "But I'm done now. Here, I can return it to you."

Maple handed the book over to June, but June did not take it.

"You liked the book, Maple?" said June, his face lit up with delight. "I've never seen you taking my math book to your room!"

"Well..." Maple searched for a reasonable excuse for bringing the book to her room, but none came to her mind. So, she decided to tell the truth. "Yeah, I guess I really do like the book. I was first intrigued by the illustrations. But the content turned out to be interesting as well, to my surprise."

"Well, I'm not surprised," smiled June. "I've always thought that you would enjoy math if you really gave it a try. You have a logical way of thinking, and unlike me, you are also a careful thinker. You'd be better at this subject and enjoy it much more than I do, Maple, if only you study it properly."

"Really? You think so?" Taken aback, Maple could not help feeling flattered upon hearing such encouraging words from her own twin brother. Even though Maple knew how talented June was in all his scientific studies and did not think she would ever be able to compete against him, hearing such an acknowledgement had a power to open her heart to an unseen possibility.

"Listen, Maple. You can keep the book. You should read the whole thing if you like it," said June. Then he added, "It's your birthday gift from me!"

Maple stared at June. Their birthday was arriving in three weeks. For a moment, Maple wondered if her twin brother was trying to save the time and energy of choosing a gift for her. But June's cheerful face showed nothing other than joy.

"Thanks, June," smiled Maple. "This is quite special for me."

"When you finish reading it, we can even discuss it!" said June eagerly.

Just then, their mother called them for dinner, and Maple and June both hurried downstairs to lay the table.

"Maple, Maple!"

Among the chattering voices in the corridor, Maple recognized a familiar voice. As she slowly came back to her senses, she saw a tall figure standing next to her. It was John, her former PhD colleague. With his clipboard in one hand and a coffee mug in the other, his casual demeanour was so much like other figures in the corridor that Maple would not have noticed him if he had not called her name.

"Hey, John! I didn't think I would meet you here today!"

"Nor did I," said John. "It's been so long since I last saw you, Maple. What brings you here today?"

"I'm attending a weekend workshop. There, in room 203. How about yourself?"

"Same here, though mine is in the conference room. I didn't know that there was another workshop going on this weekend."

The two of them stood next to each other looking over the helix staircase. Maple thought of what to talk about upon this brief unexpected reunion. After a few seconds of silence, Maple chose to take the easy option.

"How's your work going?"

"It's going well," said John smoothly. "Writing more papers this year as I should be. I submitted two papers so far. One of them got accepted by a journal already, and I'm close to finishing another one."

"Isn't that amazing? Good for you!" said Maple, trying to sound as merry as possible.

"I may go to the States next year for my postdoc," continued John.

"You got a new position?"

"Yeah, somebody at Berkeley is interested in my work and invited me to work with him."

"Wow, for how long?"

"It's a two-year contract, but there is a possibility of extension if the collaboration goes well."

"You must be excited, are you?" asked Maple with a smile. She had put a lot of effort to conjure a smile on her face, but John kept a gloomy face and sighed instead.

"I'm not sure. My girlfriend has recently got a job here. If I take the offer, we'll be far apart, and two years is a long time, you know. We are discussing different possibilities at home right now."

"Oh, I see," Maple looked down at the helix staircase. She did not know what to say about that. After a brief pause, John opened his mouth.

"How are things on your end, Maple? Are you still working at Riverside?"

"Yes, I am," Maple answered quickly. "It's a teaching position. So I'm trying to squeeze in my research here and there whenever I have time."

"How long is your contract?"

"Three years. This is my final year."

"So, do you know where you will be going next? Are you going to do a postdoc? Or will you be looking for another teaching position?"

"I don't know." Maple's eyes followed an old man in shabby

clothes who was walking up the helix staircase in front of them. "I kind of like living in Riverside. I might want to stay there."

"But can you find a job there? I thought it's a small town."

"I will, if that's what I want to. You know, it doesn't have to be academic."

"You mean, are you going to leave academia?"

John's eyes were wide with disbelief. Just then, the atmosphere in the corridor became restless. The break time must have been ending, and people started to move in different directions.

"I guess I should be going," said John. "I can't miss the next talk. But, it was nice meeting you, Maple."

"Same here." As she watched John hurrying back to his conference room along with other young and old male figures, Maple felt the empty sensation in her stomach grow bigger.

Back in the seminar room, Maple settled on her seat, with paper and a pencil ready in front of her for the last talk of the afternoon. An organizer stood up and announced the detail of the social dinner planned for the evening and asked for everybody to raise their hand if they were interested in participating.

Suddenly becoming overly conscious of her presence in the room, Maple thought hard if she should attend the social dinner or not. It was certainly a great opportunity for her to talk to other participants, get to know them, and perhaps even ask them some in-depth questions about their talks. Especially for somebody like Maple who was not regularly surrounded by researchers working in the field, it was a rare opportunity that should not be missed.

Maple lifted her hand from the table in front of her and looked around. Then she saw rows of raised hands. She could not tell from people's expressions if they were excited about the prospect of the social dinner or not. As she watched the focused but empty faces, Maple felt a wave of anxiety. Who were all these people? What difference would it make if she attended this social dinner or not? Who would even notice her presence or absence?

Soon the last talk of the day started, but Maple could not concentrate. The empty sensation had now reached every part of her body, and as she took notes with her pencil, she felt a burning sensation in her eyes. *Not now, not now, not now...*

Maple fiercely fought back her tears, but a few drops escaped onto her notes. Just when she reached to wipe away the droplets on her notes, Maple suddenly recalled the time when she first met Olive at Café Rose. At that time, Olive told her about her panic attack and how sitting inside Café Rose made her feel safe and protected.

Maple thought of Olive. What was she doing now at her home in Riverside? Reading her book over a cup of tea? Cleaning her house? Or cooking supper? Maple pictured Olive moving about in her cozy living room in the orange late afternoon sunlight coming in from the window. She imagined herself sitting with Olive in her living room talking to her. A sense of warmth slowly came back to her numb body, and a tiny smile played on her lips. Taking a deep breath, Maple turned back to the blackboard.

When the talk was over, Maple quickly collected her stuff and walked out the door, leaving behind all the people who were still lingering in the room, some discussing, some just staring at the empty space. Nobody seemed to notice her leaving, and conveniently, there was nobody to stop her or call her name.

On her way back to her youth hostel, Maple decided to treat herself with a quality dinner. It had been a big day for her, and since she was not going to the social dinner with other participants, at least she could arrange a cozy dinner with herself over her diary.

As she walked down College Street, Maple came upon a shopfront with a particularly homey atmosphere. Warm yellow lights were spilling from the glass windows onto the wet sidewalk. Inside, there were wooden tables surrounded by beautiful tiling and decorations on the walls. On the glass door, *Persian Kitchen* was written in golden lettering. Maple knew nothing about the Persian cuisine, but the restaurant's welcoming atmosphere convinced her that it was the right place for her to spend her dinner time.

The restaurant must have just opened for the evening. When Maple walked inside, she was the only customer. A tall, kind-looking lady came to serve Maple with a warm smile, and she led her to one of the tables by the window. When Maple asked the waitress for a comforting dish with vegetables, her face lit up, and she recommended a dish called *kashke bademjan.*

"It's a Persian eggplant dip - so tasty and perfect for comfort. We'll serve it with traditional Persian bread."

Once the lady was gone with her order, Maple sipped her glass of water and gazed out of the window. The numbness she had felt in the seminar room was gone and she was now back feeling like herself.

Maple took out her blue covered diary and a pencil from her bag. As she opened a new page and stared at the passing people under the darkening sky, the day's events replayed in her mind. She recalled how she left her youth hostel that morning excited for all the talks and new ideas she was going to discover. She recalled the wonder and eagerness she felt as she listened to the morning talks. Then the lonely lunch time. The short presentation she gave during teatime. The emptiness that filled her heart. The memory of a conversation with June that suddenly visited Maple while resting in the corridor. The brief meeting with John. The last talk and her anxiety attack.

Maple took another sip from her glass. There was one more day left. How excited was she for the Sunday talks? As she pictured another day of sitting in that closed seminar room surrounded by empty faces, Maple's heart sank. What was the point of doing all this? Feeling so empty? In a place where nobody noticed if she did or didn't come? If she didn't come, she was sure that somebody else would fill in her seat just fine.

"Here is your *kashke bademjan*."

The waitress' kind voice rang next to Maple, and Maple was brought back to her senses. There in front of her was a fine white plate with a smooth eggplant dip and a basket of fresh Persian bread. The gentle fragrance of the eggplant and the yoghurt whey tingled Maple's nose calling for her attention.

"Enjoy your meal!"

With a big warm smile, the waitress left Maple and went to attend an elderly couple who had just arrived at the doorstep. Maple slowly picked a piece of bread from the basket and coated it with the shiny eggplant dip before carrying it to her mouth. The moment the blissful mixture of the bread and the juicy eggplant flavoured with yoghurt whey landed on her taste buds, a smile appeared on Maple's face and a decision was made. Maple was not going to attend the Sunday talks. She would drive back home and go to meet Olive instead to spend the last moments of the weekend together.

Chapter 7

Lily

Lily was at a small bar on the busy College Street in Toronto. After the long and intense week of study, it was a moment of luxury to come to this sushi bar to grab a quick supper. As always, she was sitting at the counter table by the window. She almost never ate her food in the restaurant, but she liked to sit by the window while she waited. Lily held her bag in her arms and gazed out of the window.

The streets were packed with families and young people hanging out. Still wet from the rain that had continued throughout the day, the ground shone in different colours, reflecting the lights from the cars, shops and restaurants.

It was always these subtle moments of observation that reminded Lily how much she appreciated living in a big city. She loved the dynamic vibe of downtown Toronto which her hometown of Riverside did not have. She loved watching people of all different backgrounds walk on the streets and imagining what different dream each one might have.

The week had been busy, but satisfactory. Lily had received the results for some of her mid-term exams and essay assignments for her psychology classes, and to her delight, they all came back with good marks. She had been so nervous about the first official evaluation of her Master's Program that she had spent the past two months commuting between the library and her house even on weekends. But now that her hard work had come back with positive evaluation, Lily was ready to take some time off for the last weekend of Reading Week. She and Kevin had planned a day trip to the Algonquin Park on Sunday to spend some quiet moments in the nature enjoying the colours of autumn.

Kevin had actually suggested that they could visit Riverside to meet Olive, but Lily turned the invitation down saying that she was not yet ready to introduce them, due to the complicated situation between her and Olive.

"Maybe I could be of help," said Kevin eagerly. "To reconnect you and Olive."

Though Lily appreciated Kevin's thoughtful intention, she first wanted to talk with Olive properly before letting her know about her new boyfriend. Lily knew how much patience she had been asking from Kevin, but she could not compromise on this point.

As Lily continued to look out of the window, a family with a little girl passed in front of the sushi bar. The girl was walking between her parents, holding her mother's hand in one hand and her father's in the other. With a beaming smile on her face, the girl was saying something to her mother. Suddenly, Lily's heart yearned for the warmth of her family home in Riverside.

September 22nd. Lily would never forget the day when she received the news of her father's sudden death. It was right after her lunch break and she was about to resume her work at the design studio when she noticed her phone ringing in her bag. It was from Olive. *Strange that she's calling me at this time of the day*, Lily remembered thinking as she picked up the call.

"Oh, Lily..." It was her mother's voice, except that it sounded strangely unfamiliar. "Oh, Lily, I'm sorry to call you like this, but..." Then her voice broke. "Your dad has just passed away."

Lily remembered that there was a silence - she needed a moment to register what she had just heard. Her mother continued.

"It was a heart attack... He suddenly fell very ill this morning, and I called an ambulance. We went to the hospital, but he didn't make it... He passed away shortly after we arrived..." Lily did not remember what she said back to Olive on that phone call. All she remembered was that time stopped in that moment, and her mind went blank.

Her then colleague Kevin offered her a five-hour ride to Riverside that afternoon so that she could reach her home by evening. It was raining hard that day. Throughout the journey, Lily's gaze was fixed on the front window, watching the droplets splash on the glass one after another. Everything was blurred in her mind. Everything felt so surreal.

Just a few days before, Lily was on a regular phone call with her father. He asked Lily about her new office and her life, then dropped his voice as if to reveal a secret. In an excited whisper, he told her about the special plan he was going to surprise Olive with to celebrate their 20th wedding anniversary that December.

"I'm planning to take her somewhere beautiful she has never been, a beautiful Mediterranean seaside somewhere in Europe." When Lily pointed out that Olive did not like travelling overseas, her father laughed his usual affectionate laugh. "That's why I may need your help, Lily."

For the entire week, the house was crowded every day with friends and relatives coming over to see Robert for the last time. Olive and Lily made themselves busy with the funeral arrangements and paperwork while Leila prepared meals for them and Alan spoke with the guests. Lily was not sure if she was relieved that she could hide her emotions behind all the tasks she was handling or if she was indeed sad about it. When the funeral was over, Lily went back to Toronto. Part of her wanted to stay longer with Olive, but work needed her back.

Shortly after her return from Riverside, another surprise awaited Lily. Her first long-time boyfriend since college time suddenly broke off their relationship saying that he had fallen in love with another girl at his office. At the time when everything in her life had turned upside down, any shock of the breakup became negligible to Lily. She remembered being strangely calm and detached throughout the process. Her concerns remained at home in Riverside.

The next and the last time Lily went home was for Christmas. Only three months after her father's departure, the house felt empty without him. Lily also could not help noticing the pain her mother was going through. Even though Olive had resumed her work at Rosemary Library and she looked fine on the outside, when she was at home, it was clear that she was suffering.

Olive had lost interest in cooking, something she used to love more than anything other than books. It was the first Christmas when Olive did not want to prepare a Christmas meal. Instead, they went to Leila's place for the evening. Throughout the holiday, Olive spent days in her nightgown whenever she did not need to go outside. She would stay up late and wake up late. Lily volunteered to cook meals to help her mother – partly out of guilt for not having been able to spend more time with her earlier. Meanwhile Lily wondered if this was all of what was left of her beloved mother without her father. There were many pockets of clutter gathering throughout the house. It used to be

Robert who regularly created a mess in the house. Olive was the one who always liked to keep the place tidy. Lily could not help making a comment about it.

"Mom, Dad would be upset to see this house like this. It's so cluttered. It's as if *you* were gone, not Dad." She meant it to be a joke, but Olive's face darkened upon hearing it and she kept quiet.

Lily regretted her words, but she could not deny the surge of anger she felt in her body. She was not sure if she was mad at herself for being insensitive toward Olive, or at Olive for abandoning herself like that. Perhaps these were both just the shadow of anger she felt toward her father who had left them so suddenly without any warning.

Thus, the two-week holiday passed quickly and without much joy, the first holiday that Lily had earned from her office after a hard negotiation with her boss. The day after New Year, Lily took the train back to Toronto.

"Are you going so soon?" Olive spoke like a little girl as she watched Lily pack her bag that morning.

Since then, Lily had not visited home. Whenever she thought of home, her stomach twisted with a strong sense of guilt. Still, it was better than the pain she would have to face at home, Lily would tell herself. What was more troubling to her was the phone calls from Olive. From the day of her father's sudden death, Lily became afraid of phone calls. Especially those from her mother terrified her, and she rarely picked them up.

Lily watched a tram pass in front of her. Even through the thick glass of the sushi bar, she could hear the heavy sound of the tram rolling on the street. It was so strange to think that more than a year had passed since that nightmare situation and Christmas was again around the corner. Was she going back home this Christmas? Or would she have to come up with another excuse?

Lily thought of Olive living all alone in the empty house. Was she still spending days in her nightgown when she was not working? Was she eating well? Was she keeping the house clean? What if her health had deteriorated since she stopped cooking? What if she was depressed? Was she angry with Lily because she stopped responding to her phone calls and hadn't visited her since last year? What if Lily was not welcome even if she decided to visit home for Christmas?

Lily shook her head. She had to stop this chain of thoughts. Her therapist always told her to take care of herself first. "Your mother is going through a grief process. So are you. You first need to attend your own process. You need to feel your own feelings and emotions."

When her father was alive, Lily could share every high and low with Olive. Olive would always be there for her. The love and care she received from Olive was so deep that Lily never really suffered the absence of her biological mother. She was happy with Olive. But many things had happened to her over the past year, and she had not said anything about them to Olive. It pained Lily not to share her life with Olive and not to have her loving presence beside her.

Suddenly, Lily's phone vibrated in her bag. It must be Kevin, asking her when their supper was arriving. Lily reached for her phone and realized that the call was actually from Olive. Her eyes were glued to the name on the screen. With a racing heart, Lily thought hard if she should take the call or not.

When Lily finally reached her trembling finger to answer the call, the phone had rang out. Just then, her number was called from the kitchen counter. Lily jumped to her feet to pick up the order.

Chapter 8

Olive

Olive was sitting on the bed with her phone in her hand. She had tried calling Lily, but no answer. She tried again. With her eyes fixed on her maple tree outside the window and her lips tightly pressed against each other, Olive waited as the ringing tone continued.

Just when she thought of hanging up, the call went to the answering machine. There was a beep, and Olive was thrown into the silence of the recording period. Suddenly becoming conscious of every breath she took, Olive hesitated for a second, wondering if she should say something or not. The time was quickly passing.

"Lily, my dear," started Olive, feeling pressured by the silence. Her mouth was dry and her body felt strangely airy. "It's me, your mother."

Why am I saying something so obvious? I'm wasting my time. Olive held her phone tight.

"Are you doing well? Is everything okay?"

Olive paused. *No, this isn't what I wanted to say.* Olive felt her hand become sweaty and her mind race.

"Lily, my dear," started Olive again, standing up and walking toward the window. Her maple branches gently swayed in the darkness. "I love you. I miss you so much. I want to hear your voice..."

There was another beep and the recording ended. Olive stared at her phone for a second in a trance as a gush of emotions took over her. A sense of relief, a sense of longing, a sense of loneliness all came at her at once like a waterfall. Tears streamed down Olive's face and she sobbed hard as she collapsed on her bed.

Olive did not remember how long she cried that night. When she was tired of crying, she curled up on her bed like a cocoon. Soon, she fell asleep. By the time her phone vibrated on the nightstand, Olive was so deep in sleep that she did not even notice it.

Chapter 9

Kevin

Under the deep blue autumn sky, the bright sunshine seemed to highlight all the remaining colours on the trees of the Algonquin Provincial Park. In the parking lot next to the Barron Canyon, on the last weekend of October, the young and old were getting out of their cars, eager to enjoy the final moments of warmth, and grab the final chance to see the different colours of autumn before the long grey winter months.

Lily and Kevin climbed out of their navy Mazda wearing their thick windproof jackets and backpacks. It was late morning and the sun was already high. They were going to hike on the Barron Canyon Trail all the way up to the top and have a picnic lunch there. That was the plan.

As soon as Lily and Kevin set their feet on the trail, a cold breeze blew and caught Lily's long black hair.

"Ooh, it's a little colder than I thought!" shivered Lily. But as she said it, Kevin did not fail to notice her face lit up with joy. With a grin on her face, holding the straps of her backpack, Lily started to march ahead. "Look at the colours, Kevin! Oh, I'm so glad that we decided to come here today - it's *beautiful!*"

"Yeah, it is," said Kevin, catching up with Lily. "And it also makes us feel happy. We should come out more often, you know."

"Yes, I know," said Lily, tucking her arm under Kevin's. "I'm sorry I've been heavily caught up in my studies. I've almost forgot how *amazing* it feels to be out in nature! But now, even my legs are bouncing with joy. Look!"

Lily started skipping on the trail with her arms stretched out on both sides. As she skipped, her hair danced around under her grey woollen hat and her backpack bounced on her red jacket. From behind, Lily looked like a funny fairy from children's literature.

"You look like a fairy, Lily," called out Kevin.

"No, I'm not, Kevin," Lily replied still skipping. "I'm being a deer. A *happy* deer. Can't you see it?" After skipping for several more steps, Lily stopped and turned around. "Now, Kevin. Show me how *you* feel right now."

Kevin thought for a moment, then he started spinning along the trail with his arms wide open.

"What do you think I am?" asked Kevin as he span past Lily.

"This is hard..." Lily narrowed her eyes. "Let's see... Are you the wind?"

"Wrong! I'm being a mushroom! A *happy* mushroom!" Then he stopped and covered his eyes.

"What happened?" asked Lily as she quickly walked toward Kevin.

"My head is spinning," said Kevin. "A happy mushroom got too excited, I'm afraid."

The two of them burst into laughter. Kevin wondered how long it had been since they had had such an unapologetic explosion of laughter together.

"Let's go," said Lily, holding Kevin's hand. "We are now

back to ourselves. No more skipping or spinning, at least for now!"

Lily and Kevin walked in peace for a while observing and taking in the surrounding nature. They watched the different colours on the trees, listened to the birds chirping and the sound of running chipmunks, feeling the crisp dry leaves underneath their feet. Then after a long and pleasant silence, Kevin finally spoke.

"So, how was your mom this morning?"

"Oh," said Lily, her hand slightly tensed. "She was fine, she just wanted to check in if I was doing well."

"Did she sound well?"

"Yes, she did," Lily replied quickly. "I was worried if there was an emergency because she usually doesn't leave a voice message. But it turned out that she just wanted to hear my voice."

"Your mom misses you, Lily," said Kevin looking ahead at a tree in front of them. A chipmunk ran up the trunk at rapid speed. "Did she ask you to come home?"

"No, she didn't," answered Lily, following the chipmunk with her eyes. "She really just wanted to hear my voice. She did say she missed me."

"And you miss *her*," said Kevin turning to Lily. "Look, Lily, we can always make a visit to Riverside on weekends. It's just five hours away from us, and I don't mind driving. You know that."

"Yes, I know, Kevin," said Lily restlessly, dropping her gaze on the patches of leaves on the trail. Kevin waited for her to say something more, but Lily was silent.

"What are you worried about?" asked Kevin at last. "Your mom misses you, and you miss her, but you two are not talking. Why?"

"It's complicated," sighed Lily. "My mom still thinks that I work at the design studio, and doesn't know anything about my breakup and my relationship with you. It's just so awkward to talk with her because I feel like I'm hiding a lot from her."

"Well, we have to start somewhere," said Kevin in a firm voice. "If you don't talk to her or see her, how on earth will she ever know about your new life?"

"Easily said than done."

"But it's possible."

"Oh, Kevin, I sometimes hate your optimism!" Lily stopped and put her hands on her waist. It was her way of showing irritation, but Kevin continued.

"But it's true. If you don't want to call her or visit her, you can still write to her. And you haven't done that yet."

Lily was silent. With her head slightly lowered, Lily looked more sad than angry. Just when Kevin wondered if he had pushed Lily too far, she opened her mouth.

"I don't want to upset her, Kevin," said Lily, her voice suddenly sounding sorrowful. "If you had seen my mom from last Christmas, you would know why I'm being so hesitant. I had never seen her so - *broken*. She was barely the same person after my dad passed away. So broken and fragile like a snowflake. One more surprise and she would have collapsed altogether. That's how she looked."

Kevin stood next to Lily motionless, feeling each tremble of Lily's heart like his own.

"I sometimes get really mad at my dad," Lily continued in a shaky voice. "For leaving us so suddenly without any notice. Especially my mom. How could he leave her for good like that? My dad meant the world to my mom."

"Lily..."

Kevin slowly and carefully reached for Lily's shoulder. He wondered if Lily would resist, but when his hand touched her shoulder, she leaned in. As he gently pulled her into his arms, Kevin saw Lily quickly wipe away her tears.

"Lily, I know you don't always like my optimism," said Kevin, carefully choosing his words, "but your dad might have created a new opportunity for you and your mom."

"What do you mean?"

"Well," said Kevin and paused for a second. Above them, a group of trembling aspens were shedding their yellow leaves, which gently danced through the air like soundless rain. With nobody around them, the stillness of nature seemed to sink into the depths of their existence. Kevin was embraced by a profound sense of security, and he hugged Lily tightly with that warm energy he felt within.

"What I mean is that you and your mom are now in a place to get to know each other anew perhaps even in a deeper way than before."

Lily was quiet and Kevin continued.

"If your dad had been alive, you and your mom might have just carried on, not making much effort to really learn about each other. I mean, that's certainly the case between me and my mom. We haven't made any effort to get to know each other beyond what we already assume about each other."

"Wait, Kevin, you've just said something important." Lily looked at Kevin, her eyes wide with attention. "Say that again?"

"I said that this awkward situation between you and your mom right now could be a chance for you two to really get to know each other," said Kevin slowly but clearly. "You might be feeling like you've lost something you had before, Lily, but what if you haven't? What if this is just the beginning of a new relationship between you and your mom? Perhaps there are things your mom didn't yet know about you, and things you didn't know about her. What if this is a chance for you both to discover something new and important about each other?"

"I've never thought of it that way," said Lily, awestruck by the new vision painted in front of her. "I've never thought of it that way. A new chance..."

Lily looked up to the sky through branches of trees. There was a new sparkle in Lily's eyes. A few hikers passed by, smiling at the scene of a young couple standing still and holding each other for a moment of revelation.

"Wow, I feel so relieved now," said Lily, closing her eyes and taking a deep breath. "You're right, Kevin. I was afraid that I lost something so precious and could never retrieve it. I was *so* afraid. But if this is a new chance for me and my mom, I don't want to miss it."

Lily and Kevin started to walk again. Lily eagerly continued.

"I think I'll write a letter to her."

"That's a good idea, Lily."

"But don't expect me to write it quickly," said Lily turning to Kevin. "I'll need to spend at least a week. I have to first organize what I want to tell her, you know."

"Of course, Lily, you must take your time," said Kevin smiling at Lily's serious face and new enthusiasm. "But do you think we will be ready to go home for Christmas?"

"That's my goal, Kevin," smiled Lily. "I'll tell her about you in the letter so that she won't be surprised when we visit her." Then she added, "But when you meet her, be prepared for a bombardment of questions! My mom is going to ask a lot of questions about you and me, I'm sure. Her curiosity knows no bounds!"

Kevin laughed. They were approaching the lookout on the clifftop.

"Let's see who will get there first!" shouted Lily and started to climb up the rocky path. "A happy deer or a happy mushroom?"

Kevin stood there for a moment, watching Lily's red jacket swiftly move up the passage, light and happy. *She does look like a happy deer*, smiled Kevin to himself before he also started to climb up the final stretch of the trail toward the lookout.

Chapter 10

Maple

Highway 401 was as busy as usual. It was Sunday, so many people were taking a day trip or visiting somebody in a neighbouring city. In addition to trucks and other commercial vehicles, there was also a large flow of regular cars on the highway. In her old black Volkswagen, Maple was sipping her now cold coffee, holding the steering wheel with one hand and looking ahead at the road. It was already lunch time, and she was starting to think where to stop for a small break to eat her lunch.

In the back, Bach's Goldberg Variations was playing. It was one of her favourite albums, the 1981 recording by Glenn Gould. As she listened to the clear sound of the piano and hummed to the music, the traffic suddenly slowed down in front of her. Maple quickly pressed the break pedal and in no time, the traffic came to a halt around her. It was not clear from where she was to see what was exactly happening on the road. Feeling restless, Maple cautiously followed the other vehicles and proceeded slowly.

After going on like that for about ten minutes, suddenly a

car accident was revealed on the road. A white car was turned upside down next to a huge truck. The glass was shattered and the frame of the car was distorted by the shock of collision. There was an ambulance and a few police cars surrounding the accident site. A person was carried on a stretcher and several paramedics were operating between the damaged car and the ambulance.

Maple felt her breathing become fast. Suddenly, her heart was pounding and she could not think of anything. She gripped the wheel tight so that she would not faint and lose all control over her body. Then, she heard a voice in her head. *June. June, June, June!*

This continued for what felt like a very long time. When it finally stopped, the traffic had started to move again, and the accident site was behind her. The quiet sound of the piano was echoing in the car, gently guiding Maple back to her senses. Maple's mind slowly started to function again, but her heart was still racing and her hands and legs were shaking. *I need a rest*, thought Maple. *I need a rest!*

Just then, her eyes caught an exit sign. Exit 611 Kingston. Maple steered onto the right lane and held onto the wheel with both hands as her car slowly carried her out of the highway.

Chapter 11

Search for Clarity

On Sunday afternoon, Olive went to Café Rose as usual. The weekend visit to the French café bakery had become Olive's ritual, and it was now unthinkable not to go there even without Maple. Olive took her usual window seat and savoured her cappuccino and croissant over her diary Orion and her mathematics book. After about two hours, Olive left Café Rose and did her grocery shopping at the grocery chain on Main Street, then walked to her bus stop. The amber sunlight was filling the late afternoon air, and there was a sense of quietness to it.

As Olive waited for her bus, a little girl - probably around the age of five or six - walked by with her mother. They had a Golden Retriever puppy with them, which very much reminded Olive of the dog her family used to keep when she was little.

The girl was having a tantrum. She was crying and shouting something at her mother. Her curly hair was messy and her eyes were red from the intensive crying. Her mother looked solid and determined. She did not look cold, but it was hard to tell her feelings from her face. The mother knelt down and tried to console her little daughter, but after some unsuccessful attempts, she took the girl's hand, and started to walk away, half pulling the girl. The puppy trotted beside them faithfully.

Suddenly, Olive felt her stomach churn as a distant memory came back to her. Like a wind from the past, it swirled inside her body and stirred up what she had long forgot about.

Olive was about to turn six when her father suddenly became ill one day. Her mother took him to the family doctor, then to a hospital while Olive waited patiently at home. When they came back home to Olive after what felt like eternity, her father looked very tired and her mother's eyes were red.

Many things changed in Olive's house that day. Her father left his job and her mother started to work full-time instead. There was a newly opened shopping mall in town, and she took a job as a tailor there.

Even though Olive knew that her father was ill, she was still happy to spend more time with him at home. They ate breakfast together before Olive left for school, and when Olive came back home in the afternoon, they sat for tea and snacks while Olive told her father everything that had happened at school. Often, Leila came to join them and the three of them would chat and laugh for a long time until Olive's father finally announced that it was time for him to prepare supper.

When Olive's mother came back home in the late afternoon, she was usually tired and grumpy, but her mood always improved over dinner, and then the family would sit together watching TV in the front room. Whenever Olive's mother dozed off on the couch, Olive's father put a blanket over her while Olive curled up next to him. Then they would talk in quiet voices until it was finally Olive's bed time.

It was one such day when a neighbour came to the door with a newborn puppy. Her dog had just given birth to four puppies, and she was looking for people who could adopt them. Olive's mother was against the idea at first, but after Olive's father said that the dog would keep him company when he was alone at home, she eventually agreed to take one.

The puppy was named Luna. Luna had a particularly lively presence, and after a while, even Olive's mother began to love the dog. Every evening, she and Olive drove to a nearby park to walk Luna. Olive secretly looked forward to this evening stroll because it was a rare moment for her to talk with her mother, who was now barely at home.

One cold winter evening, Olive and her mother were walking Luna as usual. Under the darkening sky, Olive was talking to her mother about her day - how she learned to spell a new word, what story her teacher told the class, what she and her friends did during their lunch break. Luna was trotting right beside them.

Suddenly, her mother stopped and turned around. Olive also stopped, excited to hear what her mother thought about her story. In her memory, there was a long pause before she finally heard her mother's voice.

"Olive, will you please be quiet?" She said with crossed arms. "I'm tired."

That moment, Olive's entire body froze. She even forgot to breathe. She stood on the spot without blinking, without breathing, and without thinking anything. Luna kept on trotting ahead of her.

"What are you doing, Olive? Come quick!" Her mother's voice rang through the cold wind. "Daddy's waiting for us!"

Olive started to cry. Her tears quickly became icy on her

cheeks, but she did not care. She stood there in the snow crying with her head facing the sky. She heard Luna running back to her, but her mother did not come back.

"Mommy!" Olive cried. She cried so hard that her voice broke. "Mommy!" She did not remember how many times she called until finally her mother walked back to her. When Olive looked at her through the thick tears, there was no smile on her mother's face. She looked weary.

"Olive, we don't have time for this." She sighed. "Let's go."

And that was the end of it. She grabbed Olive's hand firmly, and started to walk back home. Olive followed her, still sobbing, while Luna trotted along cheerfully.

It was strange that Olive thought of that particular evening from her childhood all of a sudden. Until this very moment she had even forgot that it had ever existed. Olive was fond of cherishing old memories, but only the happy ones. That evening walk was one of the more painful events she had with her mother. Olive's mother became harsh on Olive when her father became ill, but their relationship grew better and closer after his death. They made plenty of happy memories together. So, why all of a sudden, did this memory come back to Olive?

Olive was so deep in thought that she did not realize when an old black Volkswagen pulled up in front of her. As she gazed into the distance, Olive heard a familiar cheerful voice next to her.

"Olive, Olive!"

When Olive looked around searching for the source of the voice, she saw Maple waving at her from the car window with a beaming smile.

"Maple!"

Surprised and delighted at the same time, she stepped toward the car.

"I thought you were in Toronto!"

"I was!" answered Maple. "But I finished early and came back home earlier than I had thought! Do you want a ride, Olive?"

Olive looked at the two large grocery bags in her hands, then turned to Maple.

"I would love that, Maple, if you don't mind these bags."

"I have plenty room in the back! Come on in, Olive!"

Olive stored her grocery bags on the backseat and slid into the car next to Maple. Maple began typing in Olive's address on Google Maps. Inside the car was warm, and the air carried a faint fragrance of citrus. When Olive looked around, she found a real orange sitting on the cup holder. She had never seen actual fruit being used as air freshener.

"OK, we're ready, Olive!" Maple's clear voice broke the silence. The next moment, the car started moving and music played from the speakers. The lively, full sound of piano filled the air. It was the beginning of Bach's Italian Concerto. Olive was startled and looked at Maple.

"This is Glenn Gould, isn't it?"

"Yes, it is!" Maple glanced at Olive with a surprised look on her face. "You know him, too? He's my favourite pianist! The first place I visited since I moved to Toronto for my graduate studies was his childhood house in the Beaches. I'm really crazy about him!"

Olive felt a ball of heat in her chest.

"My husband also loved listening to his piano," said Olive in a quiet voice. "You two really have so many things in common."

"You know, Olive, I feel as if I had actually met your husband in my life," Maple smiled. "Hearing all your stories. I feel the same way with Lily, too, even though I haven't yet met her."

Olive swallowed as she remembered something she had been meaning to tell Maple about.

"Speaking of Lily, I have something to tell you, Maple. She called me this morning," said Olive. "You know, I haven't heard from her for quite a while. But this morning, she called me."

"Wow, Olive," said Maple, her eyes widening with excitement. "That's great news! How did it happen?"

"Well," said Olive, straightening up in her seat. "Last night, I gave her a call, and as usual, she didn't pick up. This time, I left a voice message. I just said I missed her and wanted to hear her voice."

Maple nodded as she steered the handle. They turned off Main Street onto a quiet street in an old neighbourhood with brick houses and spacious front gardens.

"This morning, Lily called me. She wanted to know if I was doing okay."

"That's lovely, isn't it?" Maple leaned forward with excitement. "And what did you say to her?"

"I said," Olive paused and looked at Maple. "I said I was well and I said I loved her and missed her so much." Then she sighed. "That's all I said. I was so overwhelmed that I didn't get to ask about her. It was a short phone call anyway. Lily was in a hurry preparing for a little road trip with her friend. But she sounded well."

"I'm so happy for you, Olive," said Maple, her cheerful voice embracing Olive like a blanket. "I'm sure Lily was happy to hear that from you!"

The car was approaching the corner where Olive's house was. Olive quickly thought of the contents of her grocery bags and her fridge at home. Was there anything special she could cook tonight?

117

"Maple, would you like to come for dinner tonight?" said Olive as the car pulled up in front of Olive's house and Maple stopped the engine. "I mean, if you have time," she added quickly. "And it's not that I have prepared anything special. In fact, nothing is prepared at the moment."

Maple's face lit up, and she put her hands together in front of her chest as she turned to Olive.

"Really, Olive? Am I invited?"

"Certainly!" said Olive. "If you don't mind assisting me in the kitchen, because you're such a great help. We could have shepherd's pie if you like?"

"Oh, Olive, I would love that! Everything you've said!" beamed Maple.

Maple helped Olive to carry the two large grocery bags inside the house, and while Olive unpacked everything into the fridge, Maple started slicing the potatoes.

"So, how was your workshop?" asked Olive as she knelt down in front of the fridge.

"Oh, it was fine. I gave a talk yesterday," said Maple chopping the potatoes. "I met one of my old colleagues there, and we chatted for some time."

"That sounds nice," smiled Olive from behind the fridge door. "I'm tempted to ask what these talks were all about, but I'm sure it's beyond my comprehension!" She laughed. "I was actually thinking of you today, Maple. When I went to Café Rose this afternoon, I looked for you even though I knew you were not coming."

Maple was pouring water in the pot, but closed the tap upon hearing Olive.

"Really? I was thinking of you, too, Olive, during the workshop."

"What? During the workshop?" Olive pulled herself out of

the fridge and turned to Maple. "Don't tell me that I was a distraction!"

"Oh, no, it's not like that," said Maple hurriedly. "I was feeling a little stressed at one point, and that's when I thought of you. I thought of you having tea and biscuits at home. And it brought me a sense of warmth and peace."

Olive blushed with both embarrassment and joy. She did not want to be a disturbance to Maple's academic activity, but felt flattered that somebody had found comfort in thinking of her. "I'm honoured to hear that I was of help to you, Maple." Then she quickly turned back to finish the rest of the unpacking.

Maple placed the pot of potatoes on the stove and turned on the heat.

"Olive, you seemed to be deep in thought when I found you on the street. What were you thinking?"

"Oh, that?" Olive had almost forgot about it. "I was suddenly remembering something from my childhood. Something I had forgot about for a long time."

"What was it?" Maple's eyes looked at Olive expectantly.

"Well..." Olive thought back on the memory. The sting rose again in her chest. "It was a memory of when I was little and my mother scolded me very harshly one day." Saying it out loud felt strange. "It happened years and years ago when I was about six. And yet, when I remembered it this afternoon, every detail was so vivid that I felt as if it had happened only yesterday."

Maple was quiet, cutting an onion and looking deep in thought. Olive pulled out another chopping board and started cutting the carrots.

After a brief silence, Maple replied, "I had a similar incident this afternoon." Slowly chopping the onions, she continued. "When I was driving on the highway this morning, I suddenly remembered the day my brother had the accident."

Olive stopped what she was doing and looked at Maple. She noticed that her cheerful expression had faded and her posture was slightly more rigid. Olive waited for Maple to continue.

"It happened more than fifteen years ago, and I haven't thought about that day in years. But this morning, I happened to witness the site of a car accident on my way, and as soon as I saw the truck and the damaged car, the memory of that day came back to me."

Maple asked Olive for a pan and waited for the oil to sizzle as she continued.

"It was during a summer break. We were all at home. June was going on a special math summer camp that day."

"A math summer camp?" repeated Olive. "Was your brother also a mathematician?"

"*He* was the one who was really good at the subject," said Maple, carefully stirring the onions in the pan. "Though he wasn't going to become a mathematician. Because he wanted to become a doctor."

"Oh, I see," said Olive, looking at the pieces of carrot on the chopping board.

"But because he was so good at math, his teacher suggested he participate in the special training session for the Math Olympiad."

"Wow," exclaimed Olive. "That sounds like a big thing. Is that a math competition or something?"

"Yes, it is," nodded Maple. "It's supposedly the most prestigious international math contest for high school kids in the world. My brother wasn't so into it at the beginning, but after a while, he started enjoying it. I guess he liked discussing questions with other participants. He made good friends. He even told me that I should also join! But I refused."

"Why?" asked Olive, completely forgetting about the carrot pieces. Maple picked them up and added them to the pan.

"Because I wasn't good at math!" laughed Maple. "I was more of a slow and careful thinker. You know, math people are usually fast; their brains work fast. At least, that's what I thought. I didn't think I could be good at it."

"But Maple, you *are* a math person," interrupted Olive as she threw in some peas and corn into the pan.

"I guess I am now! Not that my brain works any faster than before!" said Maple and fell silent for a while. After waiting for a moment, Olive asked Maple.

"And what happened on the day of accident? You were going to say something about that."

"Oh, yes, I almost forgot where I was heading with all this," said Maple slightly startled. The potatoes were ready and Maple started to mash them as she carefully chose the words. "That morning, June left home early. He and other participants were going to travel to Whistler by bus, that's where their camp was going to be held."

Olive looked at Maple, who was mashing the potatoes with a determined face.

"My mother and father woke up early to see him off. I didn't. They shouted to tell me that he was leaving. But it was Sunday, and I was too lazy to wake up that early." Maple kept pressing the potatoes with the masher. "I heard him go and fell asleep again. A few hours later, my mother woke me up. And that's when I learned about the accident."

Olive held her breath.

"We were told to come to the hospital where he was taken. When we arrived, we learned that June didn't make it. He was already unconscious when they discovered him. When the bus fell off the cliff, he was crushed underneath the seating." Maple paused and took one long breath. "I never saw the site of the accident. My parents wanted to protect me from any further shock, and didn't allow me to go with them when they went to visit the site shortly after the accident. But I kept thinking about the place of the accident, and imagined how it must have happened."

Olive heard a tremor in Maple's voice. She slowly reached out her hand and placed it on Maple's shoulder. Maple turned to Olive to smile, but a tear fell down her cheek.

"I don't know why," said Maple quickly wiping away her tear. "I get emotional over this even now. It happened a long time ago, you know. I've already made peace with it."

"But it doesn't work like that, Maple," said Olive gently embracing Maple into a hug. "Our memories of people. There's really no timeline to it. One day, it feels far away, and the next day, it can feel as close as yesterday. It's like that."

"I do think of June a lot," said Maple in a muffled voice. "I don't talk about him often because people usually don't talk about death. But there are many days when those memories feel like only yesterday, you know."

"Yes, I know," said Olive quietly. She thought of the evening when she heard Robert's voice and felt his presence around her, and of her sudden memory of her early childhood that afternoon. "I know exactly what you're talking about."

Olive added the ground lamb into the pan. Silence fell as the meat sizzled in the pan with the other vegetables and Olive cleared away the kitchen counter. Once everything was cooked, Olive transferred the content of the pan to a casserole dish and Maple topped it with the mashed potatoes. Then everything went into the oven. Now all they needed to do was to wait.

As the two of them walked over to the dining table to sit, Olive realized that she had left Robby's earth globe and a rubber band on the table. Earlier in the afternoon, she had been playing with them again to find the answer to the mysterious question about the circle.

"Why do you keep a globe on your dining table, Olive?" asked Maple intrigued.

Slightly embarrassed, Olive decided to tell Maple the truth.

"I've recently found a very interesting puzzle."

She told Maple about the mysterious question that she had found in the library as she sat down across from Maple.

"It goes like this. You are standing inside a circle on the ground. How can you move out of it without crossing the circle itself?"

A flicker of delight crossed Maple's eyes. "Do you like these types of questions, Olive?"

"Well, I like puzzles," said Olive. "But this one's difficult. I've been thinking about it for a while now, but I still don't have a clear answer."

Olive told Maple about all the different ideas she had tried. When she explained the experiment that she had tried on Robert's globe, Maple's eyes widened in surprise.

"These ideas you've been trying are all interesting. And I hope you don't mind me saying this…" Maple took a deep breath. "You're demonstrating great mathematical thinking here."

There was a pause. Olive was confused. "Maple, I'm not solving a math problem. How can I be thinking mathematically?"

"Oh, Olive, mathematical thinking is not just for solving mathematical questions!" Maple's voice raised with excitement. "It refers to a systematic way of thinking designed for effective problem solving."

Facing Olive's still puzzled expression, Maple took another deep breath. Her eyes were now twinkling with curiosity. "Anyway, Olive, I'm interested in hearing your conclusion."

"My conclusion?" repeated Olive blankly. "I don't have any conclusion, Maple. That's the problem."

"Well, I think you do," said Maple. "From what you've observed in the experiment on Robby's globe, how would you answer the original question?"

Olive was completely baffled. But not wanting to spoil the excitement on Maple's face, she started to think out loud.

"Well, my idea is to imagine that we are standing on a globe and try to answer this question from that perspective. Do you see the dot representing the city of Toronto? Imagine you are standing there. Now I place this rubber band on the globe so that it makes a circular loop around Toronto."

"Okay," said Maple, placing the rubber band on the globe. "Now Toronto is inside the loop. The puzzle asks us to find a way to move out of this loop but without crossing the loop itself."

"That's right," said Olive. "Keep picturing yourself standing at the position of Toronto while I explain you the procedure, okay?"

"Okay," nodded Maple, her eyes focused on Toronto. Olive took a deep breath and began to explain.

"Now, I'm going to stretch this rubber band to make the loop larger," said Olive, stretching the rubber band with her hand. "I make the loop larger and larger." Olive stretched the rubber band as much as she could. Now the entire American continent was contained inside the loop. "I make the loop even larger until it hugs the entire circumference of the globe." Olive carefully stretched the rubber band so that it hugged the circumference of the globe. They were now at the turning point of this whole process.

"Now, I push the rubber band to the other side of the globe just a little so that it can start shrinking," said Olive, pushing the rubber band in the opposite direction from where it started.

The moment it was no longer hugging the circumference, the rubber band shrank rapidly. Soon, it was back to its original size resting on the Australian Continent.

"Here comes the mysterious part," murmured Olive as she carefully slid the rubber band on the globe's surface from Australia across the Pacific Ocean until it came closer to Toronto. "Okay, Maple, imagine once again that you are standing on the globe where Toronto is located. Tell me, are you now inside or outside of the loop?"

"Well, I'm now definitely standing outside of the loop!" Maple's face lit up with delight.

"And did you cross over the loop throughout this process?"

"No, Olive!" said Maple. "I was standing at the position of Toronto throughout the process, and even though you were moving the loop around, I never came in contact with the loop, and so, I never crossed over it either!"

Maple clapped her hands.

"So that's your answer, Olive! In this way, we can start from standing *inside* a loop and come out of it *without* crossing over the loop itself!"

But Olive was still concerned. "I'm still not convinced," said Olive. "It somehow feels like cheating to me, Maple. What bothers me most is that the meaning of inside and outside of the loop isn't made very clear at the beginning."

Maple's eyes widened. "Can you tell me more about it?"

"Well, I asked myself how I normally distinguish between inside and outside of something," Olive began carefully, concentrating on her thought. "Then I realized that there is always a border that separates one side from the other. For example, inside of a house is separated from the outside by a wall."

"That's true," nodded Maple.

"For this question, we can think that the loop plays the role of a wall. But then I face an issue," Olive paused and sighed.

"Usually, when we use the term 'inside,' we picture an enclosed space, don't we?" Olive was speaking very slowly now reflecting upon each word she said. "When I place the loop on the ground, it's clear which side of the loop is enclosed. That's what we usually call *inside* of the loop."

Maple nodded quietly.

"But when I place the loop on a globe," Olive shook her head. "Something strange happens... Both sides of the border, I mean the loop, are enclosed! Think about it!"

Olive looked at Maple seeking for help, but Maple was so focused on listening that Olive felt compelled to continue.

"So, the next thing I do is that I stop using these ambiguous terms *inside* and *outside*. Instead, let's pay attention to the fact that the one side of the loop contains Toronto and the other side doesn't. I can call the side containing Toronto 'T-side' and the other side 'O-side.'"

"Great idea," said Maple.

"The T-side and the O-side are both enclosed in the globe, but only one of them contains Toronto, namely the T-side."

"That's right," nodded Maple.

"But then if I adopt this point of view, nothing really changes even after doing the stretching and shrinking process of the loop we did before."

"What do you mean?"

"I mean, as I stretch the rubber band, the T-side of the loop gets bigger and the O-side gets smaller. But if I look at Toronto itself, it stays on the T-side throughout the process. Actually, the situation remains this way unless we cross the loop over Toronto. But that's forbidden in the question."

Maple was quiet. Olive sighed. "So basically, I don't know if I've really answered the question. Throughout this loop stretching and shrinking process, Toronto remains on the *same side* of the loop. So, I don't think I can say that Toronto moved from *inside* to *outside* of this loop in this process, can I?"

"That's it," said Maple. "That's your complete answer to this question."

"What?" Olive stared at Maple, confused. "But it doesn't sound like one."

"Not all questions are expected to have a yes or no answer, Olive," said Maple. "Especially when the question itself contains ambiguity, our job is to first clarify where lies the ambiguity. But you did exactly what needed to be done," said Maple holding Olive's hand. Sometimes, her gesture reminded Olive of Leila.

"You clarified the ambiguity of the original question by pointing out that the term 'inside of the loop' was not well-defined on a globe and instead defined the notions "T-side" and "O-side" of Toronto. Then after stretching and shrinking the loop on the globe, you observed that Toronto remained on the *same side* of the loop throughout the process. But nonetheless, it looked as if Toronto came out of the loop without crossing over the loop itself."

Olive slowly started to see her point. It was as if a dense fog had cleared and she found herself standing on a mountain top.

"Wow!" said Olive. "I've really answered the question?"

"Congratulations on your wonderful demonstration of mathematical thinking!" exclaimed Maple now holding Olive's hands. Olive grinned. It felt like such an accomplishment that she felt too elated and energized to sit still. Olive started to dance in her chair to express her excitement and Maple followed her lead when the oven beeped. Maple and Olive burst into laughter. Their dinner was ready.

Chapter 12

Search for a Better Way

I t was a very cold day. The heavy, overcast sky of November was hanging low outside the window of the tiny loft of Orion Bookshop. The sun had already set, and the people on the street were walking briskly toward their destinations in the fast-spreading darkness. Inside, Olive was sitting at a small table reading *Take A Number: Mathematics for Two Billion*. The place was warm and quiet, and neither the cold air from outside or the noise of the busy passersby did not seem to affect Olive. With a small smile on her face, Olive was absorbed in her reading.

It had become a habit for Olive to visit the secret loft of Orion Bookshop after work and spend an hour of quality time with herself over a cup of coffee. Occasionally, she would take her eyes off the book, sip her coffee and look out of the window to reflect upon her thoughts. Then Olive would realize how short the day had become, how all the leaves were gone from the trees, and how the way people dressed themselves had changed over the past two months. On such occasions, she could not help but feel how nature was moving on and how she was part of it.

As Olive gazed out of the window, a strong wind blew and a tiny white flake landed on the window glass. Olive leaned and moved closer to the window. Another flake landed right in front of her nose.

"Snow!" exclaimed Olive. "It's the first snow of the winter!"

There were footsteps coming up the staircase, and the lady from the bookshop appeared with a plate in her hand.

"I've just seen the first snowflake of the winter!" said Olive to the clerk unable to hide her excitement. Surprised, the lady walked over to the window in an elegant motion and checked the snowflake herself.

"It's that time of the year again," she said and smiled at Olive. "Would you like to try our scone?" The lady placed the plate in front of Olive, on which a beautiful round scone was emanating a wonderful smell.

"Oh," said Olive, immediately captured by the treat. "That's so tempting. How much is it?" Olive reached for her purse, but the lady waved her hand.

"Oh, don't even mention it! I've just had a craving for scones. I would feel better if you could also have one. Just have it."

The lady walked back downstairs without waiting for Olive's reply. With the company of a delicious scone and coffee, Olive went back to reading.

Today, Olive was reading a chapter on multiplication. Olive knew how to multiply two small numbers from what she learned in school, but in the book, Lillian was explaining to her how to multiply not just positive integers but also negative ones. Olive had also learned this in middle school, but it was something that she never fully understood. And since there were not many occasions in her daily life where she needed to multiply negative numbers, Olive had simply forgot about them.

Lillian started by reviewing the multiplication of two positive integers with the example of 2 times 3 equals 6. You could think of it as adding 2 three times 2+2+2, thus obtaining 6 as the result. There was nothing new about it. This was exactly how Olive understood multiplication.

Then Lillian moved on to the multiplication of one positive integer and one negative integer with the example of -2 times 3. Again, you could think of it as adding -2 three times: (-2)+(-2)+(-2) = -6. *Sure thing*, thought Olive.

Next, Lillian changed the place of a negative integer in the multiplication. Instead of doing -2 times 3, she now did 2 times -3. It did not make sense to add 2 "negative three times." That was when Lillian invoked the rule "Commutative Law for Multiplication."

The night before, over a cup of rooibos tea and chocolate biscuits, Olive was reading the chapter called "The Rules of the Game." In this short chapter, Lillian listed five rules which governed how addition and multiplication - the two operations that every child learned at school - worked. These five rules seemed to repeat quite obvious things about addition and multiplication except that Olive had never seen them explicitly written like this.

Rule (1): *The Commutative Law for Addition.* If you add two positive numbers, even if you reverse the order in which you add the two numbers, the outcome remains the same.

$$a+b = b+a.$$

For example, 3+4 and 4+3 both give us 7.

Rule (2): *The Commutative Law for Multiplication.* The same rule as above, but this time it is for multiplication.

$$ab = ba.$$

For example, 2 times 5 and 5 times 2 are both equal to 10.

Rule (3): *The Associative Law for Addition.* If you add three positive numbers, either if you add the first two numbers first or if you add the last two numbers first, the outcome is the same.

$$(a+b)+c = a+(b+c).$$

For example, try to add the three numbers 2, 7 and 11. If we first take the sum 2+7, which is 9, then add 11, we get 20. Meanwhile, if we first take the sum 7+11, which is 18, then add it to 2, we get 20 again.

Rule (4): *The Associative Law for Multiplication.* The same rule as above, but this time it is for multiplication.

$$(ab)c = a(bc).$$

For example, if we first multiply 2 and 3, which is 6, then multiply by 4, we get 24. Meanwhile, if we first multiply 3 and 4, which is 12, then multiply it with 2, we get 24 again.

. . .

Rule (5): *The Distributive Law.* If we first add two numbers then multiply the result with a third number, the outcome will be the same as when we first multiply each of the first two numbers with the third number, then add them up.

$$a(b+c) = ab+ac.$$

For example, if we multiply 5 by the sum of two numbers 2 and 7, which is 9, we get 5 times 9 equals to 45. Meanwhile, if we first multiply 5 and 2 and multiply 5 and 7, then add up the two numbers, we get 10+35=45, the same answer as before.

These five rules felt so obvious to Olive that she did not understand why Lillian had to create a separate chapter to explain them in detail. Olive yawned, closed the book and went upstairs to prepare to sleep.

Olive stared at the line 2 times -3. She could not think of it as adding 2 "negative 3 times," but now, Lillian invoked the rule "Commutative Law for Multiplication". Because the result of multiplication of two numbers did not depend on their order, 2 times -3 was equal to -3 times 2, which we could think of as adding -3 twice and get -6 as the answer.

Finally, Lillian explained how to multiply two negative integers with the example of -2 times -3. Olive took a bite from her scone and leaned forward, concentrating. *Well, I can't think of it as adding -2 negative three times. But even if I swapped the order and make it -3 times -2, I would still have the same problem. So what should I do in this case?*

At this point, Lillian switched to letters. She asked Olive to look at the following three-term addition:

$$ab+a(-b)+(-a)(-b).$$

This looked rather strange. Olive wondered why all of a sudden Lillian brought up this strange addition. What did it have to do with -2 times -3?

Lillian did not answer Olive's question right away. Instead, she invited Olive to invoke the rule "Distributive Law" from the previous chapter on the last two terms of the three-term addition.

$$a(-b)+(-a)(-b) = \{a+(-a)\}(-b) = \text{o times } (-b) = \text{o}.$$

Therefore, she wrote, the value of the original three-term addition is $ab+\text{o}$, which is simply ab by omitting the zero. Lilian then continued:

$$ab+a(-b) = a\{b+(-b)\} = a \text{ times o} = \text{o}.$$

Therefore, she wrote, the value of the original three-term addition is $\text{o}+(-a)(-b)$, which is simply $(-a)(-b)$ by omitting the zero. Olive stared at these for a while. She could see how the rule "Distributive Law" was used and she agreed with the equations, but she still did not get the point of this whole procedure.

Finally, Lillian did something that felt like a trick. In front of Olive's eyes, Lillian equated the two values:

$$ab = (-a)(-b).$$

And she concluded that -2 time -3 is equal to 2 times 3, which is 6. Olive blinked. *Wait, how did that happen? That was so quick.*

Olive shifted her body in the chair trying to read the page again when she caught the glimpse of her watch. It was already ten past six. She was so absorbed in the reading that she did not realize the time. Surprisingly, the lady working in the bookshop had not yet come to announce that the store was closed. Olive jumped to her feet, sipped the last drop of her coffee, and threw the book into her work bag. Then she stumbled down the staircase with the coffee cup and the plate in her hand and a sentence of apology ready on her tongue.

When Olive came down to the bookshop, however, her apology flew away. The small floor space was full of half-opened boxes of books. The woman was leaning over one of them, pulling out the contents and writing down something on her clipboard. Wearing a refined burgundy dress and surrounded by the sea of boxes, she looked like a princess lost in a desert island.

"Um..." Olive opened her mouth, trying to decide what to say next. The lady was startled to find Olive in front of her, but quickly returned an elegant smile.

"I'm sorry I didn't notice you coming. I was dealing with something here." She pointed to the boxes around her. "These were supposed to arrive earlier this afternoon, but there was an accident on the road, and they arrived late. So, I'm checking the contents just now." She smiled again.

Olive looked around. There were at least twenty boxes yet to be opened.

"Do you do everything by hand? I mean, don't you use a barcode reader if you're registering them to your shop?" asked Olive.

The lady's face clouded over and she sighed. "Actually, the

store computer system broke just before the boxes arrived, and the repair person won't come until tomorrow afternoon. So, I have to at least check the titles and count their numbers before closing the shop so that I can be ready for tomorrow morning. It's life, you know."

"Let me help you," said Olive putting down her bag on the back counter and walking towards the lady. When she opened her mouth to protest, Olive raised her hand to stop her. "Don't worry, it's not because of your scone, though it was incredibly delicious! I'm a librarian, so I'm quite used to this sort of task. I spend so much time in your shop, it's the least I can do." Olive smiled. "By the way, I'm Olive."

"I'm Stella," said the lady extending her arm to shake Olive's hand. "You're very kind, Olive. But it will take a long time, and I don't want your family to wait for you at home."

Stella's sincere eyes caught Olive's, and for a moment, Olive's thoughts travelled to her empty house. She had not even decided what to cook for supper yet. But nobody would bother if she came back home late... because there was nobody waiting for her at home and nobody needed to know her whereabouts. The familiar void crept up Olive's body. She thought of Robert and Lily.

"My family wouldn't mind if I came back home a little late," said Olive at last. Her voice came out strong, surprising Olive herself.

"Are you sure?" asked Stella glancing at the clock and turning back to Olive.

"Yes, I'm sure," replied Olive with a broad smile.

"You're very kind, Olive. Then I shall accept your offer to help."

The two of them started to work together. Olive read out the titles, the prices, and counted the number of each title while Stella jotted them down on her clipboard. At first, Olive opened each box and counted the books one by one. But then she realized that sometimes the same title could be found in more than one box. Olive decided to open all the boxes first, and collect all the books under the same title in one place. In order to make things easier, she also gathered the same titles in piles of five. Now she was ready to count.

"You're so methodical and organized, Olive." Stella was watching Olive closely over the boxes. "It's impressive." Then she turned back to her clipboard. Olive paused for a second, staring at the piles of books in front of her as she felt a distant memory come back to her.

Olive was eight years old. At school, her class was learning the multiplication table. They had been working on it for a few weeks, and they were almost at the end of the lesson. That week, she and her classmates were learning the multiplies of nine.

Though Olive had a great memory with words and excelled in English, it was not the same way with numbers. It required much time and effort for her to visualize each number and feel comfortable with it. At home, Olive had drawn a complete multiplication table with crayons on a big sheet of paper and pasted it on the wall of her room so that she could practice reading the multiples on her own. She wanted to make sure that she could show her progress to her teacher by the end of the lesson.

At the beginning of each class, Mr. Robinson, her teacher, would ask the class for volunteers to read out the multiples of a number that they were learning during the week. The last couple of times Olive had volunteered, she was not chosen because there were several others who wanted to do the task and there was time only for a few.

So, this week, Olive was all the more determined to volunteer to read out the multiples of nine in front of the class. It was her last chance to show her teacher how much she had learned about multiplication before they moved on to the next lesson about division.

One evening, Olive was memorizing the multiplies of nine in her room. She was able to memorize all the way up to 9 times 7 after many efforts, but then she kept struggling to remember 9 times 8. Olive would repeat "9 times 8 is 72" many times before starting again the whole read-out from 9 times 1.

Olive was so focused on the task that she did not hear when her mother called Olive to bring supper to her father. Due to his illness, Olive's father had been staying mostly in bed for a few months by this point. Olive was about to read out the line "9 times 8 is 72" when she saw her mother's angry face at the door.

"How many times do I have to call you?" she barked at Olive. "I asked you to bring supper to your dad."

"I'm sorry, Mommy." Olive quickly apologized. "I was practising the multiplication table. I'm coming now."

Just a moment before, in her imagination, Olive was bravely standing in front of everyone in her class reading out the multiples of nine. But now, all the excitement was gone and only a sense of guilt filled Olive's body. With her head down, Olive quietly followed her mother to the kitchen and picked up the tray of supper.

When Olive entered her father's bedroom accompanied by Luna, he was quick to notice the dismay on Olive's face.

"What happened, my dear?"

Olive did not reply. Without looking at his face, she placed the tray in front of him and turned to leave, but he stopped her.

"Come here, Olive. Sit with me."

Olive looked at her father. He looked much weaker than the man she had remembered from a few years ago before his illness, but his eyes were full of warmth and affection just like before, if not more. Olive sat next to her father while Luna curled up on the carpet next to the bed.

"I was practising the multiplication table," said Olive.

"Oh, you were!" said her father, gently putting his arm around her. Olive felt comforted.

"We'll be doing the multiples of nine tomorrow at school," she continued, looking up and feeling satisfied to find that her father was listening to her and smiling. "My teacher will ask us to read them out, so I'll do it in front of everybody."

"Wow." Her father's eyes widened just enough for Olive to anticipate the next line. "You're such a brave girl, Olive." He hugged Olive with as much strength as he had. Olive wished that she could stay in the moment forever.

"Can you read them out for me, Olive?" Her father asked, as he straightened himself up on the bed. "Since I won't be able to watch you do that at school tomorrow?"

Olive was delighted. She nodded enthusiastically and started to recite.

Everything went well until she reached 9 times 8. Then she stopped. She could not remember the number yet again. Her father saw Olive's struggle in her eyes.

"You're doing great, Olive."

"But I'm not finished yet!" Olive was close to tears. She wanted to show her father that she had learned *all* the multiples of nine.

"Olive, do you remember the multiples of eight?" asked her father gently. Olive nodded. "What is 8 times 9?"

Olive searched for the answer in her memory. To her relief, she found it. "72."

Her father nodded. "9 times 8 is the same as 8 times 9. So, if you forget 9 times 8, you can think about 8 times 9 instead."

A light of hope shone in Olive's eyes. "9 times 8 is 72," said Olive. Her father was smiling, the smile that Olive adored and would remember long after his death.

Just then, an angry voice echoed in the corridor. "Olive!" It was her mother calling her for supper. Olive jumped to her feet. She did not want to hear her mother say "How long does it take just to bring supper to your dad?" So, she had better hurry.

As she turned to leave, her father took Olive's hand. "Good luck tomorrow." He reached out from the bed and kissed Olive on the cheek. "And don't worry about your mother. She's not upset with you. She's only upset with me being sick in bed." Olive nodded though she did not understand him. He was the greatest father in the world, so how could her mother be upset with him?

The next morning, Olive sat next to Leila on the school bus as usual. She wanted to practice the multiples of 9, but Leila wanted to talk about the school trip planned for the next week. Olive did not argue. She sat there, half-listening to Leila and anxiously holding her school bag on her lap until their bus journey finally came to an end.

When the class started that morning and Mr. Robinson asked for volunteers to recite the multiples of nine, Olive's hand shot up high in the air before anybody else's. Mr. Robinson saw it, and perhaps he even noticed the confidence in Olive's eyes.

"All right, Olive. You're the first. Go ahead and recite for us."

Olive stood up. She felt the whole class watching her. Slowly, she started to read out the multiples of 9. Everything went smoothly until she came to that dreaded line. "9 times 8 is..." Olive paused. The number had escaped her memory once again. But Olive did not panic. She only needed to recall 8 times 9 in her head. "8 times 9 is..."

Olive remembered her father's bedroom. She was sitting next to him. He was smiling. He was proud of Olive. He told her that if she forgot 9 times 8, then she could remember 8 times 9 instead.

"8 times 9 is..." Olive searched everywhere in her memory for the answer. She would find it because she had found it yesterday. Olive recalled her mother's angry face. She was yelling at Olive, and her father told Olive that it was not because of her but because of him. Olive was unable to speak.

"That was a good try, Olive." Mr. Robinson's voice sounded from a distance. "That was a very good try indeed."

"But I'm not finished yet!" Olive wanted to scream, but no sound came out of her mouth. She just stood there speechless, feeling the burning silence of the class on her body. Her face had turned crimson, and her hands were sweaty, clutching her skirt.

"You can sit now, Olive." Mr. Robinson smiled and continued as if nothing had happened. He asked the next person to recite.

Olive collapsed on her chair. She heard the class applaud when the person after Olive successfully completed the multiples of nine. Olive felt a burning sensation in her eyes. She quickly blinked back her tears and clutched her skirt tight. There was another round of applause, and another girl completed the read-out. Mr. Robinson's voice rang in the classroom.

"Great job, everyone! I think multiplication has become easy for you. Today, we will begin the lesson on division." Olive did not recall what happened in the class after that. Somehow her brain had shut down and she could not think of anything.

From that day on, Olive started to fall behind in mathematics. It was not that she stopped making an effort to understand the materials because she really did. But something changed that day when Olive had to sit down before completing the multiples of nine in front of the class. It was as if something was broken inside her.

That year, shortly before the Christmas holiday, Olive's father was taken to the hospital in an ambulance. He suddenly lost consciousness while preparing to sleep. Olive waited at home as usual, thinking that she would see her father again soon when he got better. But to her surprise, he did not come back home this time, not in the way she had imagined at least. It was the first death Olive had ever encountered in her life.

When the new year arrived and Olive went back to school, Mr. Robinson called her to his desk to offer his condolence. He then looked at Olive and told her about the new system they had introduced for math lessons.

"We're now dividing the class into two groups," he explained. "One for advanced students, and one for students who need more help." Olive looked at her teacher's face without words. "I know you're a smart girl, Olive. But I see that math is not your strength." He said the last sentence with such certainty that it made Olive uncomfortable. But she did not know what to say. Mr. Robinson continued. "So, I have put you in the second group, Olive. Miss Green will be teaching the group."

The rest became a history. Through the remainder of her school days, Olive prowled through the math classes as they grew more and more incomprehensible. In high school, she focused on her favourite subjects, English and History, and tried her best to acquire the minimum credit in mathematics required for graduation. Once she entered College to become a librarian, she heaved a sigh of relief that she no longer had to study mathematics ever again.

The piles of books were staring back at Olive on the floor of Orion Bookshop. Olive did not know why she had suddenly recalled that particular memory. Just like her memory of the winter walk with her mother, this was also something Olive had carefully locked out of her mind for a long time. She had completely forgot about it until now.

Olive took a deep breath and started to count the number of books in front of her.

"5, 10, 15, 20, ..." Olive murmured to herself as she touched the piles of five from left to right.

"I thought you were counting the number of piles," called Stella from a few boxes away.

"What?" Olive looked up and lost her count.

"I thought you were counting the number of piles, not books," repeated Stella. Her eyes were following Olive's move with curiosity.

Olive looked at Stella and back at the piles. "Yes, I'm doing that, all right."

"No, you're not, you're counting the number of books! I have a good idea," said Stella and started to make piles of five in all other boxes of books. "Let's make piles of five for every book title first, then we only need to count the number of piles. That would be much easier."

In a blink, there were piles of five everywhere on the floor along with a few uneven piles.

"Now, Olive," called Stella pointing to the piles in front of Olive. "Can you tell me how many piles are there for that book title?"

"Five piles and two books," said Olive. Stella wrote down "27" on her clipboard.

"5 times 5 is 25, plus 2 is 27," said Stella and smiled at

Olive. "Now, let's do the other ones."

This way, Olive and Stella finished registering all the books in less than half an hour. When they finished, Stella thanked Olive sincerely.

"I feel I didn't do much," said Olive blushing.

"Oh, no, you gave us a *strategy*!" said Stella and pointed to the piles of books now neatly stored next to the back counter. "I couldn't have finished it so fast without it."

"But you're the one who made use of the piles," laughed Olive. "I made piles, but I was still directly counting the books, you know. I'm really not good with numbers."

"Me, too," said Stella, eagerly nodding as they both made their way to the door. "I guess that's why I tend to do things without any strategy when it comes to counting or anything related to numbers. Somewhere in my mind, I think that if I don't have a strategy in the first place, then I can avoid dealing with any piece of math." Stella opened the door for Olive. The night air was cold and they could see their own white breath. "That's what I thought at least. But today, you showed me the power of having a strategy and it wasn't scary at all."

That evening, after having a quick supper of salad, Olive went upstairs into her bedroom, and sat on her bed for a long time in darkness thinking about the memory of the day when she volunteered to recite the multiples of nine and the piles of books at Orion Bookshop. In her mind, she saw books sorted out in piles of nine. When she counted the number of piles from left to right, there were eight of them. "9 times 8 is 72," whispered Olive and closed her eyes. Tears rolled down her cheeks.

"What's the matter, Olive?"

A gentle voice sounded next to Olive. Olive listened carefully. Keeping her eyes shut, she envisioned Robert sitting next to her.

"A memory, Robby," answered Olive. "I don't think I've ever told you about this one."

"What is it?"

Olive almost wanted to reach her hand and feel the warmth of her husband, but she was afraid of losing his presence by moving. Still with her eyes closed, Olive replied.

"It's about when I was learning the multiplication table at school. I volunteered to recite the multiples of nine in front of the class, and I just couldn't remember what 9 times 8 was."

Olive waited for a response, but no voice came back. Instead, she felt a very warm presence right beside her.

"Such a small thing, but it really put me down that day. It was during the time my father was sick in bed. He heard me practice, and helped me to remember 9 times 8 by pointing out that it was the same as 8 times 9. But when I stood in front of the class that day, I even forgot what 8 times 9 was! I was disappointed in me. I wanted to memorize *all* the multiples of nine. I really wanted to make my father feel proud."

"Maybe you can do it now, Olive. Finish the last two multiples of nine for us."

"What, Robby?" Olive's eyes snapped open. Sure enough, there was nobody sitting next to her. She was the only person in the room. But Olive could not deny the sense of warmth that filled the air around her. She carefully opened her mouth.

"9 times 8 is 72. 9 times 9 is 81."

Olive's clear voice echoed in the room. As soon as she finished, an overwhelming sense of relief embraced her, and tears streamed down her face.

"Don't stop me this time, Robby, let me cry," said Olive as she rolled into her blanket. "It seems that I have lots of crying to do these days. And this is the only reasonable way I can move forward right now."

Chapter 13

Proof: Attitude of Careful Examination

That Sunday, when Maple arrived at Café Rose, Olive was writing her diary. Her face lit up as always upon seeing Maple. They exchanged hugs as always, and Olive watched Maple sit next to her and order a coffee and a pain au chocolat as usual. When this whole ritual was over, Maple and Olive turned to each other and both tried to speak at the same time. Olive saw a hint of anxious excitement on Maple's face, which very much mirrored what Olive was feeling inside of her.

"You go first," said Maple with an anxious smile.

"No, you go first, Maple," said Olive. "I can see that you have something very important to tell me."

"Yes, I do. But so do you, Olive. Your face is so focused and ready to tell me something important."

"Is it?" Olive blushed. Her left hand was clutching the edge of her skirt tightly. Olive consciously loosened her grip and smoothed out her skirt with the same hand. "Well, I just have a few questions I wanted to ask about the book you gave me."

"Oh, what is it?" Maple leaned forward, her eyes widening

with curiosity. Olive was afraid that Maple might forget what she was going to tell her about. As if to read her mind, Maple reassured. "Don't worry, Olive, I promise I won't forget to tell you my story after yours. So, go ahead and tell me your questions!"

Olive took a sip from her cappuccino and took out a piece of paper from her handbag.

"The other day, I was reading a chapter on multiplication, and she, I mean, Lillian tried to explain to me why -2 times -3 is equal to 6. From my distant memory, I do remember that when we multiply two negative numbers, the result becomes positive. But at school, we just memorized it as a rule. I'm surprised and intrigued that there is a way to explain why it has to be that way."

Olive took another sip from her cappuccino.

"I really want to understand Lillian's explanation, but it feels too complicated. I couldn't get the point even though I read the section several times already."

On her piece of paper, Olive had copied down the three-term addition Lillian used in her explanation:

$$ab+a(-b)+(-a)(-b).$$

Pointing to the addition, Olive continued.

"Instead of talking about -2 times -3, she started talking about -a times -b and asked me to consider this strange three-term addition. I don't get it. First of all, why don't we just look at -2 and -3 and directly compute them? Why all of this hustle with letters?"

Maple listened to Olive carefully, whilst sipping her coffee. After taking a bite from her pain au chocolat, she slowly began to answer her question.

"So, you're asking me why we can't compute -2 times -3 directly like we did for 2 times 3?"

"That's right," nodded Olive eagerly. "When we learned 2 times 3, we thought of it as adding 2 three times: 2+2+2, which is equal to 6. We didn't need to use letters to explain that, did we?"

"No, but that's because positive integers were where multiplication was first *defined*," said Maple and looked out of the window as if to contemplate the route she was going to take. Olive watched Maple closely. She could tell that Maple had just entered her thinking space. Whenever Maple became thoughtful, she spoke slowly and deliberately. Olive loved the quiet atmosphere it created around them. It made Olive feel as if they were about to begin an exciting adventure.

"When it comes to explanations in mathematics, Olive, there are at least two kinds," began Maple carefully. "One is a direct one, where you try to understand the reason by looking at the meaning of the thing. For example, 2 times 3 is 6 because we defined the meaning of '*a* times *b*' as 'adding *a* precisely *b* times' whenever both *a* and *b* are positive integers."

"Right," said Olive, nodding as she sipped her cappuccino.

"The other kind is an indirect one, where you try to understand the reason via logical deduction. You start from something that you already know to be true and proceed step by step to obtain the conclusion. For example, in our case, we start from what we know to be true about multiplication of positive integers and try to establish that when we multiply two negative integers, we get a positive integer."

Olive stared at Maple with a puzzled look on her face. She was not sure if she had understood the difference between the two kinds of explanation that Maple had just described. Especially, the one via logical deduction. What did it mean to proceed step by step from what was known to be true? As if to notice Olive's confusion, Maple smiled reassuringly.

"Don't worry, Olive. We're about to take a closer look at an example of a logical deduction. We will try to understand why -2 times -3 has to be *positive* 6 starting from the fact that 2 times 3 is 6."

Maple took a bite from her pain au chocolat, then continued. Her clear voice rang in the quiet afternoon coffee shop.

"You know this, Olive. In mathematics, we deal with different kinds of numbers. We start with positive integers, then learn about fractions and decimal fractions, and later on, encounter the negative version of all these."

Olive nodded carefully, her hand resting gently on the coffee cup.

"You see, Olive, in mathematics as well as in any other aspect of life, we have to be very mindful when we enter a new territory. In this case, the world of negative numbers."

Maple jotted down '-2 times -3' on the piece of paper Olive had placed between them.

"Let's start by recalling what we know. We know how to multiply two positive integers. For example, 2 times 3 is 6. Like you said, we think of it as adding 2 three times: 2+2+2 is equal to 6. This is how we *defined* multiplication in the first place. If a positive integer a is multiplied by another positive integer b, we understand it as adding a precisely b times."

"That's right." Olive nodded eagerly.

"Now, Olive, we are leaving our familiar situation and moving into the world of new numbers, namely, negative integers," said Maple and took another bite from her pastry. "It's really like travelling to a new country. We have to be careful not to assume things that we don't yet know about. Nothing is more hazardous than moving about in a new place assuming that things work the same way as they did in our old place. Just because people drive on the right side in our country, we cannot assume that it's the same in the new country we visit. So, we'd better be careful, right?"

Olive nodded. She had once read somewhere that in Japan cars drove on the left side of the road.

"For us, it's important to acknowledge that at this moment we know very little about these new numbers called negative integers. The only thing we know about them is their meaning. That is, we know that if we add a negative number to its positive version, they cancel each other out and we get zero. For example, (-2)+2 is 0 and (-3)+3 is also 0. Are we happy with this?"

"Yes, I do understand that," said Olive sipping her cappuccino.

"Great. But here is the thing. We don't yet know how to think of *multiplication* among these new numbers. The only case we do know about is when we multiply a negative number by a positive one, like -2 time 3. In this case, we can think of it as adding -2 three times. And if we already know how to add two negative integers, we get (-2)+(-2)+(-2) equals -6. But otherwise, we run into a problem. Think about 3 times -2, for example."

"Is it because we cannot add something negative times?" asked Olive, thinking back on what Lillian had told her in the book.

"Exactly. It doesn't make sense to add anything negative times. Adding 3 negative twice. What does that mean? Such a concept doesn't exist!"

"But what if we switch the order of the multiplication and did -2 times 3 instead?" asked Olive, trying to remember what she had read in the book.

"Ah! Now, you're starting to use a toolbox to go around this problem, Olive," said Maple, her eyes carrying a mischievous smile. "But you have to tell me what tool you are using. On what grounds are you allowed to switch the order of our multiplication?"

"Well," said Olive taken aback by the seemingly obvious question. "I thought we can switch the order of multiplication without changing the outcome. For example, 2 times 3 is the same as 3 times 2, isn't it?"

"I see," said Maple and sipped her coffee. "You're talking about the Commutative Law for Multiplication. Yes, that was certainly a valid rule in the world of positive integers. So, are you suggesting us to import that rule to the world of negative integers?"

Olive hesitated. Until now, she had never questioned that what she could do with positive numbers she could do with negative numbers as well. But hearing Maple's question, Olive wondered if that was the wrong thing to do.

"What do you think, Olive?" Maple's twinkling eyes were gazing at Olive expectantly. Olive took a deep breath.

"Yes, I thought that the rule applies not just to positive integers but to negative integers as well. I thought that we can switch the order of multiplication even when the multiplication involves a negative integer. But it now feels that I've made a blind assumption. I shouldn't have assumed that."

"No, that's not a blind assumption, Olive!" Maple's voice bounced with excitement. "When we venture into a new territory of numbers, we can choose to carry over the set of basic rules from our first world of numbers. Remember the list of rules Lillian gave us in the book? One of them, the Commutative Law for Multiplication, says that the outcome of multiplication between two numbers doesn't depend on the order in which we multiply them. We carry over that rule to the territory of negative integers. So, yes, we can think of -2 times 3 instead of 3 times -2!"

Olive was quiet. Something bothered her, even though she did not know how to put it in words. Finally, she opened her mouth to speak.

"I'm a little confused, Maple. You said that we cannot yet assume anything about negative integers except for their meaning. But you say that we can choose to carry over the set of rules from our original world. Why is that an okay thing to do?"

"Such a good point, Olive," said Maple putting her hands together in front of her. "But it *is* an okay thing to do. In fact, this is exactly what we do whenever we venture into a new territory in mathematics. We first decide on the rules we want to carry over to this new territory, then observe the consequence of those rules in detail. That's when we start seeing what's actually happening in this new territory."

Seeing that Olive was not yet fully convinced, Maple asked.

"Remember when Lillian said that mathematics is like a game?"

"Yes, I do," nodded Olive with a smile. "At the very beginning. Actually, that's what inspired me to read the book even though I had zero confidence in my mathematical ability. I like card games and board games, and some of them I play really well!"

"Great," smiled Maple. "So, think of multiplication as a game, Olive, with a certain set of rules. The original card set was positive integers, but now, we are adding a new set of cards, namely, negative integers."

"Okay."

"We keep the rules the same. But we don't yet know how these new cards will behave in the game until we actually start playing the game."

"Oh, I see." Olive looked out of the window, trying to verbalize her thoughts. "So, we *can* keep the rules. What we don't yet know and cannot assume is the *behaviour* of our new cards."

"That's exactly right."

"So, how does that apply to our case?" Olive turned back to her piece of paper. Maple had written a new line which read '3 times -2.' "Since we are keeping the set of rules Lillian gave us in the book, we *can* use the Commutativity Law for Multiplication, can't we?"

"Yes, certainly," said Maple and wrote '3 times -2 = -2 times 3.'

"Then we can now think of it as adding -2 three times," said Olive elated. "That's (-2)+(-2)+(-2), which is equal to -6!"

"Wonderful, Olive!" Maple wrote '=-6' to complete the chain of equations. "This case is now solved. Let's record our achievement here," said Maple and wrote:

$$a(-b) \text{ is a negative integer.}$$

"This is just a way to remember that a positive integer times a negative integer gives us a negative integer as a result." Maple explained to Olive, who was closely watching Maple's writing. "*a* and *b* stand for any positive integer. Because what we've just discussed applies to any pairing of a positive integer and a negative integer."

Olive nodded. She used to hate seeing letters in mathematics at school, but now, it felt like a perfectly reasonable thing to do.

"Okay, Olive," Maple's excited voice rang out next to Olive. "Now we are ready to tackle your original question. We are about to see *why* -2 times -3 has to be *positive* 6!"

Olive sat up straight on her chair. The posture reminded Olive of the time when she was about to make an important move in a strategy game. She was excited and nervous at the same time. "I'm ready."

"So, this time, we need to think further, because changing the order of this multiplication doesn't give us any break-through. It will still be a negative integer times a negative integer."

"That's right," nodded Olive. "And this was when Lillian started talking about this mysterious three-term addition."

"Right, let's see..." Maple looked at the three-term addition which Olive had written on the piece of paper:

$$ab+a(-b)+(-a)(-b).$$

"Yes, this looks a bit complicated, but it's actually a common practice. Once we learn this particular process, we'll be able to apply it in many other situations. So, it's worth learning it."

Olive found it funny how the way Maple talked about these pieces of mathematics sounded so casual and matter-of-fact. It was as if they were talking about steps in a new cooking recipe or a direction to a new grocery store in their neighbour-hood. Olive wondered if perhaps there was nothing lacking in her ability and that with proper practice she was capable of navigating these seemingly difficult mathematical arguments just like anything else in her life.

"But before we dive into figuring out the actual move, let's take a second to recall what conclusion we are expecting to see at the end." Maple's clear voice rang again next to Olive, and Olive was brought back to her senses. She saw Maple grab her last piece of pastry and throw it into her mouth. Olive took hers and did the same.

Once the last piece of pain au chocolat was gone, Maple

spoke again. "The conclusion we are expecting to see at the end is this," said Maple and wrote:

$$(-a)(-b) = ab.$$

"Again, a and b stand for any positive integers. We want to see that when we multiply two negative integers, the result is the same as multiplying their positive versions. Do we agree?"

"Yes." Olive nodded. "If this is true, then we get -2 times -3 = 2 times 3, which is equal to 6. I agree that this is the conclusion we are hoping to get."

"All righty," said Maple and pointed to the three-term addition on the piece of paper. "Let's first look at the last two terms of this addition, shall we?"

Maple wrote down the last two terms of the three-term addition on the paper:

$$a(-b)+(-a)(-b).$$

"Do you see that both of these terms end with 'times -b'? This means that we can pull out 'times -b' outside like this."

$$a(-b)+(-a)(-b) = \{a+(-a)\}(-b).$$

"This is the rule of Distributive Law mentioned in Lillian's book," explained Maple, eyeing Olive reassuringly. Olive was listening carefully.

"But adding -a to a gives us zero. So we get this," continued Maple and wrote:

$$a(-b)+(-a)(-b) = \{a+(-a)\}(-b)= 0 \text{ times } (-b) = 0.$$

"In this way, we learn that the last two terms in the original three-term sum add up to zero. This means that the three-term sum itself is actually equal to *a* times *b*!"

$$ab+a(\text{-}b)+(\text{-}a)(\text{-}b) = ab+\circ = ab.$$

"This is the first milestone I wanted to achieve!" said Maple putting down her pencil. "Just now, we successfully discovered that this mysterious three-term sum is equal to *a* times *b*."

Olive stared at the last line. She agreed with the equation, but she did not see the point of doing all this. If the three-term sum was equal to *a* times *b,* what really was the use of dealing with this complicated sum in the first place?

"Are you wondering why all of this hustle?" asked Maple as if reading Olive's mind. "If it was going to be equal to *a* times *b,* Why did we need to bring up this three-term sum in the first place?" said Maple sipping her coffee quietly. "But here's the thing, Olive. This three-term sum is actually very interesting. We are about to see that it not only equals *a* times *b*, but it also equals *-a* times *-b*!"

In front of Olive's puzzled eyes, Maple continued her writing:

$$ab+a(\text{-}b) = a\{b+(\text{-}b)\} = a \text{ times } \circ = \circ.$$

"This time, we are looking at the first two terms of the three-term sum," explained Maple. "You can see that I again used the rule Distributive Law by pulling out the common factor *a* in the front. Adding *-b* to *b* gives us zero, and anything multiplied by zero equals zero. This way, we see that the first two terms of our three-term sum add up to zero. What does this tell us about the three-term sum?"

$$ab+a(-b)+(-a)(-b) = o+(-a)(-b) = (-a)(-b).$$

"See what's just happened. The three-term sum is actually equal to $-a$ times $-b$! But we already knew that it's equal to a times b from our previous computation, didn't we? So this means," said Maple cheerfully and wrote down the last line:

$$ab = (-a)(-b).$$

"We have reached our conclusion."

With that, Maple put down her pencil and sipped her coffee. Olive felt very close to understanding something new, but she did not yet quite grasp the whole picture of this argument. It was frustrating. She quietly went through the chain of equations on the paper once again. Then after a long silence, she finally opened her mouth to speak.

"So, this mysterious three-term sum was the key somehow," said Olive contemplating. "It's equal to both a times b and $-a$ times $-b$. That's how we got our conclusion. The three-term sum was like a bridge."

"Yes, that's exactly right, Olive," Maple beamed. "That complicated-looking sum was the bridge we needed to connect a times b and $-a$ times $-b$."

Olive sighed.

"Well, Maple, this is awfully clever, I must say," said Olive, then sipped her cappuccino. "I feel as if I were watching a magic show, except that unlike a magic show, every step was shown in front of me and I agreed with each step. And yet," stopped Olive and stared at the piece of paper once again. "It's wondrous to see how a sequence of these obvious steps can lead us to this kind of useful conclusion. We have just explained why a negative integer times a negative integer has to be a positive integer using a few obvious rules!"

"What we have just seen is an example of a *mathematical proof*, Olive," smiled Maple. "I said earlier that there are two kinds of explanations in mathematics. A mathematical proof is the one where we start from what is known to be true and proceed by taking logical steps to get to the conclusion."

"A mathematical proof..." Olive sipped her cappuccino quietly, looking at the chain of equations on the piece of paper and listening to Maple carefully.

"I want to tell you something very special, Olive," said Maple, leaning over the table and turning to Olive. "Have you ever wondered about a mathematician's bread and butter?" asked Maple, her eyes round with excitement. Olive had barely thought of a mathematician until she met Maple, let alone had she ever wondered about their bread and butter.

"No, Maple, I haven't."

"Well, then, let me tell you what they are - statements and proofs!" beamed Maple. "A mathematician's important role is to come up with a new statement, then try to prove that it's true by building a mathematical proof."

Olive sipped her cappuccino listening carefully while Maple continued.

"A statement is often called a *theorem* among mathematicians. A theorem captures some meaningful perspective in its statement. For example," said Maple, pointing to the chain of equations on the piece of paper between them. "Here, in our example, the statement says that a negative integer times a negative integer gives us a positive integer. That's a meaningful perspective, isn't it? Like we said earlier, at first, we didn't yet know how multiplication looks like for negative numbers."

"Right," nodded Olive slowly.

"But every statement in mathematics has to be supported by a mathematical proof. We have to verify if the statement is actually true by constructing a logical argument starting from what is known to be true along with a set of basic rules."

Olive nodded, gently holding her now empty cup with her both hands.

"In our example, we started from what we knew about multiplication between positive integers and built our argument using the list of basic rules Lillian gave us in the book."

"Right," nodded Olive eagerly with a smile.

Maple sipped her now cold coffee and looked out of the window. Suddenly, a hint of sadness crossed Maple's face, or so thought Olive.

"You know, Olive, mathematical proofs teach me an important life lesson. They teach me to be careful with any given statement that I encounter in my life."

Olive was listening intently. Maple continued.

"When I was in my final year of college, I was thinking of taking up graduate study in mathematics because, well, I really loved what I was learning and wanted to see more of what it offered."

Olive nodded. The thought of Maple at her daughter's age bursting with hope and curiosity made Olive smile.

"But when I consulted with one of my professors whom I truly respected, he told me to my face that he didn't think it was possible for me to pursue mathematics at such a high level."

"What?" Olive's voice raised. "But why?"

"Well, he said that I was too slow to catch up with all the cutting-edge research stuff."

"You? Slow?" Olive could not believe her ears. Among all the people that she had met in her life, Maple was not only the kindest but also one of the brightest.

"I don't know, Olive. Looking back, I feel he might have been sexist. There are quite a few of those people even among math practitioners, I'm afraid to say." Maple shook her head.

"Anyway, I was hurt upon hearing this. It did shake my confidence, you know?"

Olive felt mad at whoever hurt Maple's feelings like that. "Of course, Maple. Who wouldn't be affected by such heartless comments? Had I been there with you, I wouldn't have been quiet for sure!"

Maple laughed upon hearing Olive's angry voice.

"But then I remembered what I had learned from math, Olive. No mathematician believes a statement completely without attempting to find a proof to support it. Here was a statement which said that I was not capable of pursuing a graduate study in math. But where was the proof?" Maple took another sip from her cup.

"Well, there was none yet. So, I decided to write my own proof. I applied to a master's program. When I completed it, I applied to a PhD program. And now, I hold a PhD in mathematics teaching mathematics at a college."

Maple looked at Olive and smiled faintly. "So, the conclusion I found in the end was that the original statement was wrong. I was capable of doing it all." Maple rested her hands on her cup. Then she looked out of the window, her eyes fixed on the now naked ginkgo tree on the street.

"Olive, people make assumptions and statements all the time including negative ones. Not only about themselves, but also about others. And many of them don't even take a moment to actually prove the statements, you know? Even mathematicians forget to do that when the statements are outside of their mathematical world. They can tell you to your face you cannot do this or that, based on the tiny portion of what they see about you."

Maple's voice was quiet but unwavering.

"But if you really practice math, Olive, you can be free from this hurtful cycle. When you find a statement that doesn't resonate with you, you don't have to believe it. You can take steps to check if it is really true or not. On the way, you will discover what you needed to know about yourself. Your true potential."

As the two of them sat in silence, soaking in everything that had been said between them, the waitress in a white apron came over to them. With a kind smile, she announced that the café had closed five minutes ago.

"Oh, my!" said Olive, jumping to her feet. "We're incredibly sorry about that!"

"Don't worry, I didn't want to disturb your conversation. It felt very important," smiled the waitress. "Take your time, I'll see you at the cash."

Maple and Olive quickly put on their jackets and cleared the table. Olive carefully tucked the piece of paper which was now full of equations into her handbag. It would always be a reminder of their conversation.

"By the way, Maple. You haven't yet told me your important story," said Olive as they both finished paying and walked out of the coffee shop into the cold autumn dusk. "You promised that you would tell me about it."

"Oh, I almost forgot!" Maple laughed as she looked up at the evening sky, which now showed several stars twinkling like diamonds. "I've decided to make a trip to the West Coast next summer before my birthday. I'll be visiting my childhood home and also the place where June's accident took place."

Olive looked at Maple motionless. Maple quietly continued.

"You know, Olive, it's been fifteen years since June died in that accident. And for all this while, I haven't visited the site even once."

Olive listened without a word.

"At first, my parents wanted to protect me from further

shock and didn't allow me to go there with them. I appreciate their intention, I really do." Maple put her hands together in front of her. "But I realized that not having seen the site myself had created a lot of fear around that day within me. Because I haven't seen it, I keep imagining what it must have been like and I get into a loop of anxiety." Maple took a deep breath. "And there's another thing - I want to honour the last moment of June's life by standing in that place and feeling everything I need to feel. Not visiting the place has created a strange emotional abyss between me and June. I don't like carrying that anymore. I want to be celebrating his life as it was."

Maple turned to Olive with a big smile. Olive smiled back. No words felt sufficient to express what Olive felt inside of her in that moment.

"You are truly a kind and strong young woman, Maple. I'm so proud of you," said Olive hiding her tears as she hugged Maple. "You'll tell me more about it as you plan for it, right?"

"Of course, Olive!" beamed Maple. "I'll be telling you everything about my trip, before, during and after! You are my friend, Olive."

That night, alone at home, Olive was washing the dishes after dinner. She had stopped using the dishwasher since Robert passed away. There were not many dishes to clean for one person, and Olive found a solace in the act of washing the dishes with her hands after each meal. It gave her a moment to reflect upon her day without too much emotional involvement.

Her gaze was fixed on the sink and she listened to the running water from the tap and the chiming of the dishes. It was not until she removed her apron, put the kettle on, placed her teacup with a rooibos teabag that she finally looked up and saw the calendar on the wall in front of her. The next Sunday was Lily's 24th birthday.

It was then and there, as she watched the circled date on her calendar, that Olive decided to make a trip to Toronto, to surprise Lily.

Chapter 14

The Details

The view from the moving train was fantastic. Olive was sitting on the window seat with her hands neatly crossed on her lap. Dressed in a white woollen sweater and dark green trousers, Olive's eyes were fixed on the window as they followed the passing scenery of brown fields, bushes and naked trees. Occasionally a river or a pond also came into sight.

Olive did not remember when the last time was that she had taken her last train trip. When Robert was alive, they always travelled in his car whether it was a leisure trip or to visit Lily in Toronto.

Leila had driven Olive to the nearest VIA railway station that morning. She had even offered to accompany Olive on the trip, but Olive refused the offer, saying that she wanted to make this trip personal and private. Truthfully, she was afraid as much as she was determined. For one thing, she was still afraid that Lily might not like her surprise visit, that she would not want to meet Olive. For another - and this was a more important reason - if Lily was willing to meet Olive and told Olive what she had been through for the past year, it might confirm Olive's ultimate fear that she had failed Lily as a mother.

"But whichever way it is, I have to find a proof," said Olive to herself. "Either I find solid proof that I'm not the mother Lily wants to be in touch with or that I am. And I'll start from there."

On the folding table in front of her, her Orion diary was placed along with her pencil. From time to time, the passing scenery brought Olive a new insight about this trip or about her life. Then she would scribble it down in her notebook. Once, the trolley came along the aisle, and Olive purchased a ham and cheese sandwich and a coffee for her lunch.

The train arrived at Toronto Union Station in the early afternoon. Olive took a subway and then a tram to reach Lily's address in Kensington Market. This was the first time Olive had been to visit Lily at this address. When Lily moved into her new apartment after graduation last year, Robert drove down to Toronto to help her, and after Lily's new place was set up, they came back home together for a family vacation in Riverside before Lily's work started in August.

Kensington Market was adjacent to Little Italy and belonged to one of the older neighbourhoods of the city. The tram carried Olive on the busy College Street to the West. As it approached Kensington Market, more and more small shops and restaurants appeared on both sides of the street, reminding Olive of an urban version of her beloved street in Richmond back home. Once she got off the tram and started to walk, she realized that it was also a residential area with many old brick houses. From rows of brick houses, a few modern concrete high-rise condos were sticking out. Olive wondered if Lily lived in one of them, remembering how she, unlike Olive, was fond of trendy buildings in a big city. But when Olive arrived at the address, it was an old three-story semi-detached brick house.

Olive pushed open the little gate and walked through the front garden, through a display of cabbages, toward the blue front door. With a thumping heart, Olive gazed at the door. She was finally going to see Lily after what felt like an eternity. There were three doorbells next to the door, and Olive pressed the one on the middle which had the room number written on Lily's address.

Olive waited for some time. When there was no answer, she pressed the button again. Still no answer. She checked the address and the room number on the piece of paper in her hand once more. They were both correct. Olive took a deep breath and pressed the button for the third time.

Suddenly, she started to feel foolish about this whole plan. She had chosen Saturday afternoon for the surprise visit thinking that Lily would not have work on weekends. But perhaps she did? Or what if she had some other plan with her friends? Now that she thought of it, Olive could not believe why she had not thought of this possibility and asked Lily's availability beforehand.

Olive was about to leave when the blue door flung open and a handsome young man appeared at the doorstep.

"How can I help you?" He asked in a kind voice. Wearing a bright orange T-shirt and grey Nike pants, he looked as if he had just come out of the gym.

"I, I, I..." stammered Olive as she searched for words. She wondered if this man lived in another unit and happened to find her at the door. "I'm visiting unit B2."

"Yes, I live in unit B2," replied the young man, puzzled. "How can I help you?"

Olive looked at his face and then at the address in her hand. "I think I'm at a wrong address," said Olive, completely confused and embarrassed.

"Show me the address," said the young man reaching for Olive's note, but Olive cut him off.

"No, I made a mistake. I'm sorry I disturbed you." Then without waiting for his response, Olive turned around and walked away.

As she walked fast, her heart was pounding and her brain was running at its full speed, trying to understand what was just happening. She walked back to College Street. There was a fancy-looking local coffee shop across the street. Without any further thought, Olive crossed the street and ran inside the shop.

Olive ordered a cappuccino at the counter and walked through a crowd of young people chatting over their drinks and snacks to find a seat by the window. A couch with a small round coffee table was available at the corner. As soon as she sat down, Olive took out her Orion diary and a pencil from her handbag. These days, whenever she needed to think about something, she wrote her thoughts down in her diary. It helped her to organize whatever was on her mind and to understand the situation better.

Olive started by writing down what had just happened.

I'm here, I've arrived at Lily's address. But when I rang the bell, a stranger opened the door and said he lived at the address.

Olive sipped the cappuccino and looked out of the window. "What a surprise that was," she said to herself. Suddenly, a tickling sensation crept up Olive's body and she let out a small laugh. It struck her as funny that she was the one surprised by her own surprise visit. Slightly relaxed, Olive continued.

What I know is that this address is correct. I recently asked Lily, and she confirmed it.

She paused and sipped her cappuccino.

But what I don't know is who that man is!

She thought back to her encounter with the young man at

the door. *He didn't look like a harmful person at least*, thought Olive. *In fact, he looked like a rather kind person from the way he spoke to me*, thought Olive further.

She let out a long sigh of relief. At least, the situation did not look dangerous or harmful. Olive then remembered his comment that he lived at the address. *If that's true*, thought Olive, *then does it mean that he lives with my precious Lily?* Olive had to take another sip in order to calm herself down. She knew that Lily had a boyfriend from her college time. She and Robert had even met him once at the graduation. But the problem was that the young handsome man she had just met was not the same person. *Could he be Lily's new boyfriend?* The answer seemed obvious, but Olive needed to check it herself to believe it. She stood up and left the coffee shop in a brisk walk.

Olive came back to the house, walked through the front garden between the rows of cabbages and stood in front of the blue door. With her head held high, she rang the middle doorbell and waited for an answer. Soon, the door opened, and the same young man in the bright orange T-shirt appeared in front of Olive. It was as if he had expected Olive to come back. He opened his arms in a welcoming posture.

"Hey, you're back! How can I help you?"

"I'm here to meet my daughter," said Olive clearly looking straight into the young man's shining black eyes. They widened as she watched and a broad smile spread across his face.

"So, you *are* Lily's mother, aren't you?" said the young man delighted.

"Yes, I am," said Olive taken aback.

The young man reached out his hand to shake Olive's. They were warm hands, and Olive felt her tension fade away.

"I *knew* you were when you first showed up! Lily talks

about you all the time! Please come in," he said and gestured Olive to follow him.

Olive was completely shocked by this unexpected turn of events. The young man spoke of Lily so naturally as if he had known her for ages, and he was not surprised at all to find Olive at their doorstep out of blue.

"I'm Kevin, by the way," he said as they walked through the narrow hallway toward the staircase in the back.

"I'm Olive," she replied, looking at Kevin's robust back as he led her up the staircase to the second floor.

"I know," said Kevin, turning back and grinning at Olive.

There was a narrow corridor on the second floor, and on the left, there was a wooden door with a golden plate that read 2B.

"I'm afraid Lily hasn't come back home yet," said Kevin as he pushed open the door for Olive. "But would you still like to come inside for tea or something? Lily told me that you like having tea in the afternoon."

"Oh!" Olive blushed. "Yes, that's true. I'd be happy to have tea with you, if you don't mind."

"My pleasure!" smiled Kevin.

The entrance led to a well-lighted dining room. From the huge window, Olive could see the front garden and its rows of cabbages. On the round wooden dining table next to the window, there was a glass vase of fresh pink lilies.

"Lily's birthday is coming up, so I brought them from a florist this week," explained Kevin, noticing Olive's gaze as he came back with a glass of water for her.

"November 24th," said Olive softly. "Tomorrow is Lily's birthday."

When Olive turned to Kevin and smiled, her eyes were watery. Kevin smiled back. Then as if not wanting to disturb

Olive, he quietly walked back to the kitchen, looking for a box of rooibos tea in the cabinet.

When he came back with a pot of tea and two cups, however, Olive was found sitting at the dining table smiling, her eyes dried and looking around the room.

"Your tea is ready," said Kevin as he sat across from Olive and placed a cup in front of her.

"Oh, thank you," said Olive, coming back to her senses. Her face lit up upon inhaling the gentle fragrance of the tea. "My goodness, isn't this rooibos tea?"

"Yes, it is," said Kevin a little proudly. "According to Lily, this is your favourite. Am I right?"

"Oh, my!" blushed Olive. "Did she even tell you that?"

"Trust me, Olive, I know more about you than you can imagine. Lily talks about you all the time. It's even hard for me to believe that this is really the first time we've met. I feel like I've met you many times already!"

"Well, that's not fair!" protested Olive. "You know so much about me when I don't know anything about you!"

Kevin looked at Olive. There was a silence.

"Lily didn't tell you about me, did she?"

Olive looked back at Kevin. His honest and sincere look pierced Olive like an arrow.

"I'm sorry, Kevin."

"Oh, no, don't apologize," said Kevin, hurriedly reaching for the teapot and pouring some in Olive's cup. "It's not your fault. I knew Lily hadn't told you yet."

"But I *want* to apologize," said Olive. Something was simmering inside of her, and she felt words pass through her throat and come out of her mouth like a bullet train. "Because it *is* really my fault, Kevin. I'm so ashamed to admit this, but I barely know anything about what my daughter has been up to over the past year." She took a deep breath. "Not just about you, but anything at all... I basically lost contact with her until very recently."

Olive held the cup in her hands and took another breath. She felt her breath shake a little. "I mean, we've texted each other and talked on the phone occasionally. But there wasn't any real communication between us, if that makes any sense."

"It does," nodded Kevin gently.

Olive took a sip from her rooibos tea and continued. "We haven't always been like this. Lily and I used to talk a lot with each other until my husband passed away last year. It all changed with my husband's death. We somehow drifted apart. I tried to keep in touch with her, but something had changed between us. Oh, you can't imagine how much I've missed her all this time!"

With that, Olive stopped talking. She quietly held the tea in her hands. Its warmth was soothing, reminding her of home. After a moment of silence, Kevin sipped his tea and slowly opened his mouth to speak.

"Well, Olive, you might be surprised to hear this," said Kevin carefully choosing the words. "But I've heard from Lily exactly the same thing. She's been troubled by the fact that she wasn't talking to you like before."

"What?" Olive looked up, her eyes wide with surprise. "Did she really say that?"

"Yeah. She always wants to talk with you, Olive. But whenever I tell her to call you, she hesitates, saying that she isn't sure how to have the conversation."

In front of Olive's puzzled look, Kevin took another sip from his tea. "For example, Lily wanted to introduce me to you for a very long time. But she keeps saying she doesn't know how to bring up the topic with you over the phone. Because she hasn't spoken with you properly for a long time, she has many things to tell you, and she's afraid she might upset you by her news."

"Upset me?" repeated Olive in a total surprise. "Why would I be upset?"

"Well, Lily knows how much you've been through over the past year. She told me how vulnerable you were feeling and she didn't want to burden you more. She didn't want to surprise you or make you worry, Olive. She wanted to explain to you properly about all the changes she has gone through so that you wouldn't have to worry about her."

Olive was speechless. Never had it occurred to Olive that Lily *wanted* to speak to Olive and that she was struggling to do so because she was *afraid* of upsetting Olive.

"Recently," Kevin continued. "We had a weekend to ourselves and I suggested to Lily that we could visit you in Riverside. But she said she first wanted to straighten things up with you before making a visit. Again, she didn't want to surprise you by suddenly showing up with a stranger - I mean, me. She promised that we would be ready to visit you by Christmas and she was going to write a letter to you. Anyway, Lily has been trying hard to figure out a way to reconnect with you. That much I know."

"I had no idea." Olive let out a long sigh. "I had no idea that Lily wanted to talk to me and that she was struggling to connect. I assumed that she was so disappointed in me that she didn't want to talk to me anymore!"

"Disappointed in you?" This time, it was Kevin whose face went blank with surprise. "What do you mean?"

"Well," Olive sighed and took a sip of her tea before continuing. "Last Christmas, when Lily came home for the holiday, I was in such a miserable state. I hadn't yet come in terms with the fact that my husband was gone, and I really wasn't functioning. Even my memory from that time is blurred. I remember Lily did a lot of housework during her stay, though. She was concerned that the house was cluttered and that I wasn't cooking much. You know, I felt really bad about that afterwards. Lily took the time to visit me, and yet, I wasn't even available to listen to her or treat her with good meals. I really regretted that."

When Olive looked up, her eyes met with Kevin's thoughtful gaze. Somehow, his demeanour reminded Olive of Maple.

"Ever since that Christmas, Lily stopped picking up my calls, and I felt that she didn't want to talk to me."

"But Lily doesn't *like* phone calls," said Kevin. "She doesn't like receiving calls because it makes her anxious. She often doesn't take my calls, too."

"Really?" Olive blinked. Here was another piece of information that Olive had not known about her Lily.

"Yeah. Anyway, Olive, I think you and Lily have got each other completely wrong. Lily wants to talk with you. She is *dying* to connect with you."

Olive dropped her gaze to the pink lilies on the table. Her eyes softened as she slowly allowed what Kevin had just shared with her to sink in. A profound sense of relief spread across Olive's body, and she felt her heart open with delight. She watched Kevin pour some more rooibos tea into her cup. Olive was touched by Kevin's natural thoughtfulness embodied in each of his words and actions. After a moment of blissful silence, Olive asked,

"So, how long have you been together? You and Lily?"

"It's been about six months now, I suppose," said Kevin, looking at Olive and smiling. "We were colleagues at the design studio. It's a small studio, so it wasn't hard to get to know each other among colleagues. We instantly became good friends."

"And when did you start dating?" asked Olive before she

could stop herself. She was embarrassed and immediately regretted being so nosy, but Kevin was not offended. He laughed instead.

"Lily's right! She warned me to be prepared for a lot of questions when meeting you!"

"I'm sorry, Kevin, but I cannot help it," said Olive. Her face was completely pink. "It's my curiosity. When I'm curious, questions just come out of my mouth before I can stop them. My mother used to scold me for that, but I guess even a mother cannot change her daughter's nature because I'm still the same!"

Kevin's laughter was contagious just like Alan's, and Olive found herself chuckling. Then she quickly added, "But my intention is never harmful when I ask these questions however embarrassing they are!"

The two of them took a sip from their cups. The tea seemed to infuse calmness in the air between them.

"I asked her out in February," said Kevin once he was calm enough to speak again. "But it wasn't until May that we actually started dating. Lily wasn't willing to at first, you know, which was completely understandable. She had been through a lot last year."

"Well, I'm glad that it seemed to have worked out though," said Olive with a smile, finishing her tea and carefully placing her cup on the table. Kevin looked up, his eyes suddenly expressing a thoughtful look.

"I'm really happy being with Lily, Olive. Your daughter is truly a special person."

Olive paused and stared at Kevin. What she saw in Kevin's eyes were nothing but his care for Lily, but Olive's heart was responding to something else.

"My daughter..." said Olive, feeling the warmth spread in her heart like the morning sun light. "She is special," smiled

Olive. "She really is."

Just then, the powerful amber light of the setting sun came in from the window and shone on Kevin's T-shirt. On it, there was a quote: *A problem is the beginning of everything.* Olive was startled. How could she not have noticed it until now?

"Kevin, that quote..."

"A quote?" Kevin looked puzzled as he followed Olive's gaze.

"Yes, that quote, your T-shirt," stammered Olive. "My friend has a sweater with the exact same quote..."

Olive remembered the day when she met Maple at Café Rose shortly after her injury. She remembered how miserable and lonely she had felt that week staying at home alone thinking about Lily's cancelled visit for Thanksgiving. She remembered how Maple told her that a problem was a gateway to a new perspective.

Two months later, Olive was now sitting in Lily's apartment in Toronto having tea with Lily's new partner. This was certainly something that would have been beyond her imagination then. Olive was now only a step away from meeting her Lily. And what about the perspective? What new perspective was she about to discover?

"I really like this quote," said Kevin. "But Lily thinks it's another example of my radical optimism."

"Well, I'm sure Lily appreciates such a quality in you, Kevin," smiled Olive. "We all need to be reminded. I wouldn't be here today if it weren't for the radical optimism of my friend who introduced me to that quote."

The room was getting dark, and Kevin switched on the light. When Olive glanced at the clock, she saw that it was already past five. It was probably better to come back again tomorrow to meet Lily.

Olive thanked Kevin for the tea and stood up.

"Are you sure you don't want to stay here for the night?" asked Kevin as he handed Olive her thick navy jacket.

"Oh, yes, I want you both to have a relaxing evening," said Olive with a reassuring smile. "I'll come again tomorrow. My train won't be until late afternoon." Then she quickly added. "But I'd love it if you could keep my visit a secret for Lily until tomorrow."

Just then, a little spider walked across Olive's shoulder, and Kevin leaned to brush it off. "Sorry, Olive, what did you say?"

Surprised by the spider, Olive forgot what she was saying. "Nothing important. Anyway, it was so nice meeting you, Kevin," smiled Olive, extending her hand. "I'll be seeing Lily tomorrow."

"Sure, Olive," beamed Kevin, shaking her hand. "Thanks for coming today."

Olive left the apartment into the cold November evening, heading to the hotel she had booked the night before. Olive was happy to be on her own for the evening, ready to relax after the long, adventurous day.

Chapter 15

Destination

It was supper time when Lily came back from the library. As she ran up the stairs, she could already smell supper. Kevin had told her earlier that day that he would prepare miso ramen for the evening. Ramen was one of Lily's favourite meals along with sushi. The thought of it made it hard for her to concentrate for the final hour of her study.

When Lily opened the door, Kevin was in the kitchen pouring the soup into two bowls.

"Did I make it in time?" asked Lily breathlessly, putting down her bag and running to the kitchen.

"I'd say *just* in time," said Kevin, distributing the noodles between the two bowls. When he looked up, Lily had come into the kitchen with her arms wide open. A smile broke across Kevin's face, which became even wider upon seeing Lily's excited face. He reached for Lily, but Lily was quicker to embrace him with a kiss.

"I could smell the supper from miles away," said Lily, closing her eyes and inhaling.

"I'm sure you did!" beamed Kevin, patting Lily's back gently before returning to the ramen bowls.

"So, how was your day?" asked Lily as she started laying the table, greeting the pink lilies in the vase as she did so.

"Well, it was quite extraordinary," said Kevin from the kitchen, turning off the fan and picking up a bowl with his both hands. "I met your mother, Lily."

Lily froze. "You did what?"

"I said I met your mother today."

"Where?" Lily looked at Kevin, her eyes wide open in disbelief.

"She came here. She wanted to see you," said Kevin, carrying the second bowl of ramen to the table. "Since you were out, I invited her for tea. We chatted for some time. She is just as unique and wonderful as you've always described her to me."

Lily was motionless. When she spoke, her voice cracked. "But she didn't tell me that she was coming."

"She wanted it to be a surprise, Lily."

"But she left without seeing me or letting me know about it? Why didn't you call me?"

Noticing Lily's desperate tone, Kevin quickly reassured her.

"She said she would meet you tomorrow."

But before he finished his sentence, Lily collapsed on her chair, completely forgetting about the dinner. Many thoughts raced through Lily's mind and waves of different emotions rushed through her body. Why was her mother, who barely travelled, suddenly coming to Toronto? Did something bad happen to her while Lily was busy with her own life? What if her mother had gotten a terminal disease or something and was here to break the news? Was she disappointed that Lily was not at home? But why didn't she even give her a call before coming? And how could she leave without seeing Lily? Had Lily hurt her mother so much that she was no longer as eager to see Lily as she used to? And was she upset that Lily was now sharing her house with Kevin, a boyfriend that she had never even heard of? Lily felt a lump in her chest. She did not know if she was sad or angry. Perhaps both.

"Your ramen is getting cold, Lily," Kevin's gentle voice sounded from a distance. Lily slowly came back to her senses. She looked at Kevin, who was sitting across from her, placing his hand on hers in silence. Lily blinked her watery eyes to clear her sight.

"I'm sorry, Kevin."

"Don't be sorry, just eat. You've been looking forward to it." Kevin handed her chopsticks.

"Thanks." Lily smiled through her tears.

The ramen was delicious. Its gentle taste reached every part of Lily's body, melting away the tension just like when sitting in a hot bathtub on a cold winter day. The two of them sat and ate in silence. Only the sound of chopsticks echoed in the room. Finally, Lily opened her mouth.

"How was my mom?" asked Lily nervously. "I mean, did she look okay?"

"More than okay, I'd say," said Kevin blowing his nose. "She was looking great."

"Really?" Lily let out a long sigh of relief. "That's good to hear."

"Oh, yes, she looked energetic. She enjoyed the tea, talked about you, and asked me a lot of questions about us just like you warned me!"

"She *does* sound well," Lily laughed. "Oh, boy, she must have been awfully shocked to find you at my address! I didn't deliver my letter to her yet!"

"I wish you had told her at least something about me, Lily," said Kevin, faking a troubled expression. "Your mother thought she came to the wrong address when she saw me and ran away. She almost didn't come back."

"Really?" Lily gasped.

"Yes! But thankfully she did come back! After maybe half an hour. And when I opened the door again, she looked so different. How to describe it? She looked determined."

"Really?" Lily looked at Kevin incredulously.

"I don't know what happened in that 30 minutes, but when she came back, she was no longer surprised. In fact, it seemed to me that she'd even accepted that you and I were together."

"Really? She wasn't upset?"

"No, not at all."

It was as if Kevin were talking about a stranger - this person who came to their door with such determination to meet her daughter, who was now living with her new boyfriend. Growing up, Lily had never had the impression that her mom was confident. She was thoughtful, compassionate, full of curiosity, but not confident. When Robert was alive, Olive used to consult him whenever and wherever she needed to make a decision, and he used to encourage Olive whenever she was unsure of herself.

"Where is she now?" asked Lily at last.

"I don't know, Lily. I didn't ask her," replied Kevin as he stood up to carry their empty bowls to the dishwasher. "But she's probably still in town. I don't think she'll go home without seeing you," he added quickly.

Lily looked down. The thought of meeting Olive in person after such a long time made her heart sing with excitement, but nervous at the same time. What if Lily met Olive and they couldn't talk properly? What if it was going to be awkward like last Christmas? Just when a hundred butterflies fluttered in

Lily's stomach, she heard Kevin's booming voice from the kitchen.

"Hey, Lily. Why don't you give your mom a call? She was really eager to speak with you. You shouldn't miss this chance."

Kevin was right. Her mother, who was not a keen traveller, had travelled a long way to make a surprise visit – all by herself. What message was she going to deliver to Lily? Lily needed to call Olive to hear her voice and arrange to meet the next day.

Olive was stretching out her feet and her entire body in the large bathtub in her hotel room. After the long day of travel and big surprises, the feeling of hot water on her skin was healing. Olive laid her head back and closed her eyes, allowing the water to gently caress her body.

"What a luxury," said Olive. Her voice echoed in the misty bathroom. As she relaxed into her body, memories from the day's journey started to reappear. Leila's thoughtful face when they departed at the station this morning. The passing scenery of fields, bushes, woods, and the shining surface of Lake Ontario. The smell of the subway. The sound of the tram. The garden of cabbages. The blue front door of the house. And Kevin. His orange T-shirt and robust back. His kind voice. The cozy dining room. The pink lilies and the rooibos tea.

"Kevin is such a nice young man, isn't he?" said Olive to herself. Though she had not yet seen Lily, it was not hard for Olive to picture Lily and Kevin being together, happy. "So, it was a *good* surprise," said Olive and smiled.

It was funny to think how Olive had expected the trip to be a certain way and how it turned out to be completely different. All the fear that she had had about this trip – especially the one of meeting Lily and then facing the reality of not being a capable mother – was completely unfounded. She did not get to meet Lily in the first place, and instead was surprised to meet her thoughtful new partner. He said many times how often Lily would talk about Olive in their conversations, which was totally unexpected given how rarely she had heard from Lily. It somehow made Olive feel less bad about herself.

"But I still need to meet Lily." She poked her feet out of the water surface. What was the purpose of her visit? "I need to tell my Lily how much I love her and how much I miss her. I'm going to tell her how much I want to be back in touch with her."

"In mathematics, it's so crucial to be always aware of what you're searching for." Maple once said when guiding Olive through the proof of why multiplying two negative integers gives us a positive integer.

"When trying to find an answer, it's so tempting to jump right into the details. But as you can see, mathematical items are complicated on the outside - look at this three-term sum, for example. So, it's easy to lose sight and get lost on the way. Often, we get lost and we don't even know what our point of confusion is. And we get into a loop."

Olive recalled the time she was reading this part of the book on her own. She was certainly confused, did not know what exactly was confusing her, and felt lost.

"But this can be avoided by being very clear about our goal. By knowing exactly what we want in the end." Maple smiled over her coffee. "It's like when you go to a grocery store with a shopping list. If you go to a store without knowing what you need to buy, you will most likely get distracted and won't buy the thing you needed."

It was such a relatable analogy.

"So, Olive, what is the conclusion we are looking for at the end?" asked Maple.

"We want to see that if we multiply a negative integer by another negative integer, it's going to be a positive integer."

"That's right. Let's write it down more precisely." Maple took her pen and wrote:

$$(-a)(-b) = ab.$$

Then she explained to Olive that their goal was to establish that the outcome of multiplying two negative integers was the same as that of multiplying their positive counterparts instead.

When Olive came out of the bath freshly dressed in her purple night gown, her phone rang on the bed. She looked for her glasses, but she realized that she had left them in the bathroom. From the ringtone, Olive guessed that it was probably Leila. She was probably wondering how Olive's trip was going so far.

"Hello?" said Olive picking up the phone and sitting down on the bed.

"Mom?" The voice on the other end sounded a little anxious.

"Oh, Lily, my dear!" Olive jumped with joy. "I wasn't expecting a call from you. Are you now back home?"

"Mom," said Lily again, her voice now stronger and somewhat tense. "Where are you now?"

"Of course, I'm at home," said Olive. "I've just taken bath."

"You already went back home?" Lily's voice was now clearly upset. There was a time in her childhood when Lily used to make a lot of tantrums. Suddenly, Olive was reminded how far they had come as a mother and a daughter.

"Why do you suddenly ask me, Lily? You usually don't call me up like this on weekends. What happened?" There was a silence.

"Kevin told me that you were here this afternoon," said Lily at last.

"Oh." Olive cleared her throat. Apparently, her visit was no longer a surprise. She needed to adjust her position. "I'm sorry, Lily. I just wanted to surprise you before your birthday. But you were out. I asked Kevin to keep my visit a secret until tomorrow, but I guess he told you anyway." Then she quickly added. "By the way, Kevin seems like a wonderful person. I had a really good time chatting with him this afternoon."

There was a silence again. Olive wondered if she had offended Lily by her silly surprise visit idea and the fact that she had been a guest in Lily's house without her permission.

Olive was about to apologize when Lily spoke again. "So, you're still in town, Mom?" Her voice shook as if trying to control her emotion.

"Yes, my dear. Is that good news or bad news?" asked Olive anxiously.

"Of course, good news! What else can it be?" said Lily. Then she started to cry. "So, can I see you tomorrow, Mom?"

"Of course, my dear! How can I go back home without seeing you? That's the whole point of this trip!"

"To see me?" There was a hint of surprise in Lily's voice. "But Kevin said that you are in town on an errand."

"*This* is the errand, my dear," said Olive. "To come and see you. I'm so sorry that I haven't done that much earlier." Olive paused. Suddenly, the thing that had been wanting to come out of Olive finally found its way out.

"Lily, I'm so sorry that I haven't been emotionally available since your dad passed away. You must have needed me as much as I needed you, but I didn't reach out. I was trapped in my own grief. I was struggling to carry on with my life without having your dad beside me." Olive took a deep breath. She could feel that Lily was listening without moving an inch.

"But over the past few months, I happened to have a new perspective of my life. I realized how much fear I was carrying about my life since long before I met your dad, and how your dad's departure made me come face to face with it. It was finally time for me to release that fear from my life. I realized I needed time for myself, Lily."

Olive was amazed by the way words just poured out from her heart.

"But I'm not here to make excuses for the mistake I made," said Olive quickly, making sure not to miss the moment to say the thing that required the most courage from her. "The truth is, Lily, I've missed you. I've missed you more than you could possibly imagine. And I didn't want to lose any more time to connect with you by hiding in my house. I want to listen to everything you have to share with me, Lily. I mean, if you're still open for that."

There was a long pause and Olive sensed that Lily was trying hard not to sob on the phone.

"Where do you want us to meet tomorrow?" asked Lily finally.

"Wherever you want."

"There's a great sushi restaurant just around the corner from my place. Would you like us to meet there?"

"That sounds lovely."

"Then shall we meet there? At noon tomorrow?"

"I'd love that, Lily."

"I'll text you the address after this, okay?"

"Sounds perfect."

It felt as though a new sense of connection was growing between them. The two of them remained silent, feeling the connection slowly fill the space between them.

"Now, you sleep well, my dear," said Olive finally, sending a kiss over the phone. "I'll see you tomorrow." Then when she was about to hang up, Lily called her again.

"Mom?"

"Yes, my dear."

"I've missed you, too. And I'm glad that you're here."

Olive's sight was blurred by tears. "I love you beyond the reach of any words, Lily."

After hanging up the call, Olive walked over to the window. It was a full moon tonight.

"I'm finally here, Robby, ready to meet our daughter."

As she spoke, she saw her own reflection in the window. A middle-aged woman in her night gown was looking back at her, her expression full of wonder and eagerness. Suddenly, Olive felt compassion for the woman in the window, standing all alone yet looking hopeful, like a little girl.

"I love you," she said to her reflection in the window. "You have people you love, and you have people who love you. I'm so happy for you."

She stood there for a long time looking at the rows of houses and the skyline of downtown, clear under the bright night sky.

Chapter 16

Theorem: A New Perspective

The sky was high and blue. The air was cold but fresh. It was past 11:30. Olive was standing in front of a sushi restaurant on College Street. Under the sign "Sushi Q," wearing her thick navy jacket, Olive was as motionless as the tree standing in front of her, and only her eyes eagerly followed the passing people on the street. As if to provide Olive with some comfort, the late November sunshine gently shone on Olive's jacket and made a puddle of light on her shoulders.

Olive had left the hotel early so that she could find the sushi restaurant without any hassle, but there was no need to worry. Located on the tram route, Olive spotted it right away as soon as she got off the tram and started walking. As she waited, a lady in a white apron came out of the door to open the restaurant for lunch. She saw Olive and smiled at her.

"Would you like to come in?"

"Thank you, but I'm waiting for my daughter," replied Olive anxiously. "She should be here soon."

"You can wait inside. We have a nice counter table by the

window. Come on in." With a kind smile, the lady motioned Olive to follow her.

As Olive stepped inside, the fresh smell of vinegar and soy sauce welcomed her. She could not help but stop and take a deep breath. Sushi was one of Robert's favourite dishes, and when he was alive, they would often go out to eat sushi together, calling it a sushi date. Olive had not had sushi for the past year, and the smell of the restaurant suddenly brought back the memories so close to her.

The host showed Olive a clean yellow wooden counter table by the window.

"You can see your daughter from here when she arrives."

"Thank you." Olive sat down and removed her jacket and gloves.

Looking out of the window and seeing the faces of people passing by, Olive felt anxious. In a matter of moments, she was finally going to meet Lily. With anticipation and excitement growing inside her, Olive was afraid that she might be crushed before Lily's arrival. She grabbed her Orion diary and a pencil from her handbag, and started to jot down her feelings.

Today is the day I'm finally meeting Lily, my precious daughter.

Olive scribbled fast.

And I'm so nervous, about to burst into tears.

Just when Olive looked up to clear her watery eyes, she saw Lily across the street. She came running over in her bright red jacket, her long black hair flying in the wind under her grey woollen hat that Olive had knitted for Lily several Christmas ago. The sunlight shone on her face; everything about her looked so lovely and perfect.

Olive raised her hand to wave at her, and stopped. She needed a moment to take in the fact that this beautiful grown-up young lady in front of her was the daughter she was about to meet. Lily noticed Olive, and waved at her.

"Mom!" Through the window, Olive saw Lily shout with a beaming smile.

"Mom!" Lily's voice echoed in the room as she came inside. She had a smile on her face which was as bright as the sunflower in Olive's summer backyard.

"Lily!" Olive cried, but her voice was muffled as Lily embraced Olive into her arms.

"Mom, I wanted to see you *so* much," said Lily hugging Olive tightly. Speechless, Olive wondered how it was possible that everything she had prepared to say had evaporated in the blink of an eye. She looked at Lily's dark brown eyes and blinked away her tears with a smile.

The lady in a white apron came back with two cups of hot green tea and menus.

"This is going to be my first taste of sushi since your dad passed away," said Olive taking a menu booklet in her hand.

"Seriously, Mom?" Lily looked at Olive with surprise. "You and Dad used to love sushi. Don't you miss it?"

"Well, from time to time, I do. But..." Olive paused. "I guess I'm afraid I'll miss your dad more if I eat sushi alone."

"I also think of Dad a lot whenever I eat sushi," Lily said thoughtfully. "But I like remembering him. Maybe that's why I go to sushi places more often than before."

The two of them laughed.

"Do you come here often?" asked Olive.

"No, not this one. There's another one down the road." Lily pointed out the window. "It's more like a fast-food restaurant. I go there often to grab a quick supper. But this place is my favourite and saved only for a special occasion like today." Lily smiled shyly and looked at Olive. "I still can't believe that you're here, Mom. You're really here."

Olive lost her words again in the overwhelming warmth brought by her daughter's presence. Not knowing what to say, she gave Lily another hug and patted her shoulder gently. "Shall we pick something to eat?"

After entertaining themselves with the wide selection of items on the menu from top to bottom, Olive and Lily both settled on the restaurant's lunch special. It came with a plate of six *nigiri* and four California rolls accompanied by a miso soup. Once the order was made, they sipped the green tea, and a silence fell between them. After lingering for a moment, Olive decided to speak first.

"I'm really sorry about yesterday, Lily," said Olive. "I really didn't mean to intrude. I just wanted to surprise you for your birthday although it turned out to be a different kind of surprise visit than what I'd thought."

"I'm really sorry I hadn't told you about Kevin before, Mom," said Lily quickly. "Kevin told me that when you saw him, you were so shocked that you left and almost never came back."

"Well, that's somewhat true," laughed Olive. "I certainly needed to take a moment to understand the situation. I didn't know that you had a new partner and that you were living together. I thought I visited a wrong address!"

The memory of the scene made Olive chuckle. Lily blushed. "But Kevin is such a lovely person - very kind and thoughtful. I really enjoyed chatting with him at your apartment." Olive smiled at Lily.

Lily's cheeks were very pink by now. She started to talk fast. "I'm so glad, Mom. I've always wanted you to meet him, but I didn't get the chance to talk to you properly..."

Then she stopped. There was a pause as they both thought of the same thing. It was Lily who broke the silence this time.

"Mom, I'm sorry I wasn't picking up your calls."

"That's okay," said Olive quickly. "I know you're busy with your work."

"Well, it's not really just that..." Lily shifted uncomfortably in her chair. Olive felt a tightening in the throat. She forced herself to speak before she lost the courage.

"I know, Lily," said Olive, trying to sound as smooth as possible. "I wasn't a very supportive mother to you since your dad passed away. I wouldn't be surprised if I was a disappointment to you and you didn't want to talk to me anymore..."

When Olive turned to Lily, she found a surprise on Lily's face. But she continued earnestly. "You know, I'm really sorry about last Christmas, Lily. You came home to visit me, but I was so unavailable caught up in my own bubble of grief. I didn't ask you about your life, I didn't prepare any special meals for you, I did nothing for you, Lily. I really regretted that after you left. I couldn't believe how I'd wasted such precious time with you when I was given the chance."

Lily opened her mouth, closed it, then opened it again. "But you never disappointed me, Mom. I'm surprised that you even thought that." She took a sip from her tea and continued. "Last Christmas, you were in a bad shape, and it was painful for me to see you that way because it reminded me how much *I* was hurt by Dad's death."

Lily's voice became strained as she tried to hold back her tears. "I also blamed myself for not spending more time with you, Mom. You might have felt better if I had stayed with you after Dad passed away, but I went back to Toronto."

"Lily, my dear..."

Olive could not think of what to say. She remembered Kevin's remark about the misunderstanding between she and Lily. Olive had certainly not dreamed of the possibility that Lily blamed herself for returning to Toronto after Robert's funeral. And that Olive's miserable state of last Christmas did not disappoint Lily but reminded Lily of her own grief over her father's sudden death. How come Olive had not thought of any of these things?

Lily continued in her shaky voice. "I've always wanted to talk to you, Mom. But many things were happening in my life, and I just didn't know how to start telling you about them. I didn't want to upset you or make you worry about me, Mom. You were already coping with a lot."

"Lily, my dear..."

"And I was so sorry for not picking up your calls," continued Lily. "I wish I hadn't developed a fear of phone calls..."

"Fear of phone calls?" For a moment, Olive remembered what Kevin had told her earlier about Lily not liking phone calls. Then Olive's heart skipped a beat as if struck by a lightning. She suddenly remembered the phone call she made to Lily from the hospital after Robert's passing. Olive clasped her mouth. How could she not have thought of that?

"Lily, is that because...?"

Lily dropped her gaze on her teacup.

"Ever since I got the phone call from you that day, I've struggled to answer your calls, Mom. Whenever you call me, my heart races and I stop functioning. I'm just so scared of hearing bad news about you."

Olive's eyes welled up with tears. "I'm sorry, Lily. I'm so, sorry..." She reached for Lily's hand. It was the same tender hand that belonged to the little girl who came to meet Olive with her father twenty-one years ago. "I'm sorry that I didn't realize that. You were keeping so much to yourself and worried about me."

Olive gently held Lily's shoulders closer to her. "But now you see that I am fine, Lily. Yes, I was in a bad shape, but I am much better now. The house is no longer cluttered and I'm cooking my meals again. And look, I'm now even travelling by myself!"

Lily let out a small laugh as she wiped away her tears. "You've never made a solo trip before, Mom."

"That's right, my dear. Remember what your dad used to say about me? That I'm tougher than what I look on the outside?" Lily laughed again. Relieved to see Lily being more relaxed now, Olive continued.

"And Lily, you don't have to explain to me everything that's happening in your life. It's not always even possible. There are plenty of things that I didn't tell my mother about, and she still came to my wedding and loved me enough to make that beautiful embroidered tablecloth for our new family."

There was a slight surprise on Lily's face as she turned to Olive. Olive continued. "All this is to say is that I *always* love you, Lily, no matter how poor my condition may look, and no matter how much you may surprise me with your news. I'm always here for you, Lily."

Olive smiled at Lily, then quickly reached for her handbag searching for a handkerchief.

"There, Mom." Lily put her pink handkerchief in front of Olive. "You always need this."

"Oh, thank you." Olive laughed as she pressed her eyes with the handkerchief. When Olive turned to Lily to return the handkerchief, Lily quickly removed her hand from her eyes and smiled with red-rimmed eyes. Just then, their plates arrived, and Lily and Olive both let out a sigh of relief to be spared from more tears.

As they started to eat, the air lightened up, and Lily and Olive became talkative. They both marvelled at the quality of the sushi – both the *nigiri* and the rolls –and talked about how it was difficult to find such a good sushi restaurant in Riverside.

"Your dad would have loved this place, Lily. I can almost hear him giving detailed comments about this lunch!"

"How do you feel, Mom? Eating sushi without Dad?" asked Lily.

"Much better than I thought," replied Olive dipping a California roll into soy sauce. "Because I'm eating it with you."

Lily smiled. Then as if suddenly remembering an important question, she asked Olive.

"Mom, did you know that you would marry Dad when you first met him?"

"What?" Olive was so surprised that she lost her balance and choked on her miso soup.

"Did you know that you would marry Dad when you first met him?" repeated Lily.

"Well, no." Olive stammered as she carefully placed her miso soup on the table and reached for her napkin. "I didn't think that we would marry at all."

"Why not?"

"Well," said Olive and thought for a while. "I wasn't exactly looking for a husband. To be honest, I had kind of given up on the idea of marriage. I was already 35, and my mother always used to tell me that I had passed my golden age." Then she quickly added. "But more importantly, your dad was still devastated by the loss of your mother – I mean, your real mother Emily. He wasn't looking for a date either."

"But that's different from what Dad told me," Lily interrupted. "He said it was love at first sight."

"No, it wasn't."

"But that's what he said!" insisted Lily.

"Well, he didn't say that to me," said Olive. "When we first met at Leila's wedding, your dad told me that he wasn't going to date any time soon because his love for your mother was deep and he didn't know when he would ever recover from the grief."

"Maybe he said that to you because he felt shy meeting you." Lily argued.

"Maybe. But it doesn't matter, Lily. We married anyway."

Lily was quiet.

Olive picked up another California roll from her plate and put it in her mouth. When she finished chewing, Lily was still silent. Just as Olive wondered if something had gone wrong, Lily opened her mouth.

"Well, it *does* matter, Mom." Her voice was fierce. "This story matters because it shows us how much Dad adored you and how much you meant in his life. And also," Lily continued in the shaky voice. "Don't refer to my biological mother as my *real* mother. It makes me feel as if you were not my real mother, and *I don't like that.*"

Olive was startled.

"I didn't mean that, Lily. It's just that..." Olive looked for words. Her heart was trembling so hard that she was afraid everybody in the room might hear it. All the insecurities of her life over the past year washed across her body like a tidal wave. The emptiness that haunted Olive for months after Robert's death. The powerlessness that plagued her whenever she tried and could not connect with Lily. Her empty house and the never-ending loneliness. The countless nights she had spent crushed under the disappointment of her incapacity to be a support to her loved ones. She remembered how many times she had dreamed of visiting Café Rose with Lily and how she had feared that it might never happen. Tears gushed from Olive's eyes. It was as if the floodgates had been opened. Everything that Olive's mind had worked so hard to keep at bay to protect Olive pushed back whatever barriers that were remaining and came at her.

"You are so precious to me, Lily. And I was afraid that I wasn't living up to the mother you deserved – somebody who is strong and capable of supporting you through anything no matter what." Olive sobbed. Her body was shaking uncontrollably. Olive did not remember crying so hard even when she faced Robert's death at the hospital. "I wanted to be that person to you, Lily. Somebody whom you can count on whenever you need." Catching her breath, Olive continued. "You don't know how much happiness and light you brought to my life, Lily. I'm forever grateful to your mother for entrusting me with you. When Robby, you and I moved into our family home, I promised myself that I would be the most loving and supportive mother who was deserving of your precious presence."

Olive grabbed her napkin and blew her nose. Then she looked at Lily, who was motionless, her eyes wide open with astonishment and her intent gaze fixated on Olive. "I felt I'd failed you in many ways over the past year, Lily –by being passive and staying at home rather than reaching out to you. I was really afraid that I might be losing you."

"Mom," whispered Lily. "But why would you ever lose me? You've never lost me, and you never will. How is that even possible, Mom?" Her voice raised. "I have two mothers, but you are my *only* mother on this earth right now. And I love you so much!" Lily looked at Olive. Her eyes were red and her gaze was fierce. "Mom, tell me that you are my mother," asked Lily.

"I am your mother, Lily," said Olive. Then holding Lily's hands, Olive said it again. "I *am* your mother."

They did not know how long they had stayed like that. When they finally wiped their faces to return to their lunch, their soups were already cold. But it could not have mattered less. Feeling reborn, the two of them smiled at each sip of miso soup and each bite of sushi as they resumed their lunch.

The rest of the time passed quickly. Lily told Olive about

her career switch and that she was now attending a training program at university to become a psychotherapist. Olive was surprised and intrigued.

"My work at the design studio didn't bring the joy I was hoping to experience." Lily explained. "I loved creating different pieces of art, but something was missing. I felt empty. In fact, since Dad passed away, I never felt like I was the same person as before. Something changed inside of me. Like, I became more aware of myself."

Lily looked at Olive, her eyes sincere and earnest. Olive listened to Lily intently. "And while I was going through my grief journey with my therapist, I got the inspiration to pursue art as a way to help somebody's healing journey. That's how I got enrolled in this special master's program." Lily sipped her tea. "I mean, there's no guarantee that this path will be the answer, but at least, I should give it a try, right? And so far, I'm loving it. I'm finding more purpose and joy every day."

Olive watched Lily speak about her life and hopes and dreams. With her head held high and her eyes fixed, she was radiant like the morning sun. It was amazing to realize how much Lily had grown over the past five years of living away from home, and how Olive had failed to notice it before.

Olive told Lily about her new weekend routine at Café Rose, her new diary practice, and her new cherished friendship with Maple.

"And guess what, Lily," said Olive. "I've started learning a little bit of math!"

Lily almost dropped her teacup in surprise. "What did you just say, Mom?"

"I've overcome my fear of math, and I'm now taking some math lessons from Maple," beamed Olive. Lily stared at Olive hard, trying to register what she had just heard. Seeing the confused look on Lily's face, Olive laughed. "I know, I'm surprised myself. My number phobia was something I thought I would never overcome."

"So, how did it exactly happen?"

Olive told Lily about Maple's exercise on perspective change at Café Rose, about the book *Take a Number: Mathematics for Two Billion*, the mysterious question she found in the library, and the concept of a mathematical proof that Maple had demonstrated for Olive.

"You know, I feel I've misunderstood math all my life. From what I learned back in school, I've thought that math was about number computation and memorizing many formulas, neither of which I was good at or interested in," said Olive eagerly. "But it's not! Math is much more than that!"

Olive sipped her tea before continuing excitedly. "Math is like a game, Lily. Numbers are the resources of the game, coming with a set of rules they are supposed to follow. And by playing the game, we can get a new *perspective* about how those numbers work. When we play the game of mathematics, one thing we are required to follow is the *logic* along with the given set of rules. And we build a logical argument from the given set of rules to obtain a new statement. This logical argument is called a *mathematical proof.*"

As she recounted, Olive recalled each discussion that she had with Maple at Café Rose and a smile broke across Olive's face. However, to Lily, who had never participated in the discussions nor read the book her mother was talking about, Olive's comment made little sense. Even so, Lily looked at Olive's sparkling eyes and listened intently, eager to understand her excitement. Olive continued.

"You know, Lily, math can be so relevant to our life, even to *my* life because it teaches me how to look at things. It teaches me to think about something deeply and follow my thought to the end. It teaches me to be always clear about what I'm looking for at the end. And it also teaches me how to examine a given statement carefully and not to fall for a false conclusion. To be honest, I'm convinced that having learned a little bit of math is an important part of the reason why I'm sitting here with you today, Lily."

"How so, Mom?" Lily's eyes widened with curiosity.

"Well, I've learned to trust myself more. Learning math is helping me to trust my thinking." Then Olive reached for her handbag and took out her Orion diary. "And writing my diary is helping me to trust my feelings and emotions. Who would've thought that these two go well together like this? Just like a cappuccino and a croissant! Or rooibos tea and Leila's lemon biscuits!"

Olive chuckled and turned to Lily. "When you come to Riverside next time, we can go to Café Rose together to meet Maple, and you will see what I mean by all this."

"Definitely, Mom," said Lily. "I want to meet Maple, too. She sounds like such a special friend to you."

"Yes, she is. And she's also looking forward to meeting you, Lily. I've told her a lot about you."

"Really?"

"Yes, Lily, and Maple says that she feels as if she had already met you a long time ago."

"How sweet."

As the two of them sat in silence, reflecting on what they had told each other, the lady in a white apron came by with two small glasses of matcha ice cream.

"Here are your desserts," she said with a smile.

"But we didn't order them, did we?" Lily looked at Olive.

"Actually, your mother told me that today is your birthday." The lady smiled at Lily. "So, this is just a small gift from us. And this," she said, picking up a big round tin from the table behind her, "is from your mother."

"Happy birthday, Lily!" said Olive, smiling and embracing Lily. "I baked a cake for you before leaving home. It's your favourite fruit cake."

Tears welled up in Lily's eyes. "You surprised me, Mom, for the third time!"

"This is a surprise visit, remember?" grinned Olive. "I hope you can enjoy the cake with Kevin tonight."

"But you are going to stay with us tonight, aren't you?" Lily quickly blinked away her tears and looked at Olive.

"I'm leaving this afternoon, Lily. I have my work tomorrow." Olive saw Lily's excitement fade from her eyes.

"Oh, Mom, please stay at least until this evening!" pleaded Lily, grabbing Olive's hand. "You've travelled so far, and I've only just met you. I want to spend more time with you!" Since her childhood, Lily was not good at goodbyes, and neither was Olive. So, instead of meeting her daughter's gaze, Olive cuddled Lily in her arms and put on a cheerful voice.

"Oh, Lily. You're now sounding like a little girl. Don't worry. I'll visit you again soon. Besides," added Olive quickly. "You have a wonderful partner. Isn't this a perfect occasion to have a special celebration between just the two of you?"

"Now, you *are* disappointing me, Mom!" said Lily, pushing away Olive and turning to her matcha ice cream. "I've looked forward to seeing you so much, and you are spending only a few hours with me on my birthday!"

Olive laughed. She could not help feeling flattered upon seeing how Lily hated to see her go. "Let me know how you liked the cake, okay?" said Olive. She was turning to her matcha ice cream when she remembered something else.

"Oh, and one more thing..." Olive reached for her handbag, took out a pamphlet, and placed it on the table between them. It was a travel pamphlet with a beautiful picture of the

Mediterranean seaside. "Have a look at this. I have an important proposal to make."

"What is it?" asked Lily, momentarily forgetting about her protest.

"Well," Olive cleared her throat. "The other day, when I was at Café Rose, I happened to find a postcard of a most gorgeous seaside. Somebody must have left it there by mistake. Anyway, the picture reminded me of the story about the Mediterranean seaside that your dad used to tell me a lot. And I thought - what if you and I travelled there together? I found this 10-day travel package to Italy. Would you like to go on a trip with me?"

Lily straightened up in her chair, completely forgetting about everything else including her last spoonful of ice cream.

"When is it?"

"It's in the second and third week of December. We'll come back just before Christmas."

Lily was quiet.

"Your dad always wanted us to visit those Mediterranean countries, but we never did. You know... I was afraid of travelling, especially oversees. But when I saw the picture of the blue sea and the colourful houses on the postcard, I suddenly felt I wanted to make this trip... with you."

Lily looked at Olive, her eyes wide with surprise and excitement.

"Mom... You won't believe this. Actually, Dad wanted to take you on a trip to Italy for your 20th Anniversary last year. And he asked me to help him with the plan."

The two of them looked at each other.

"So, this is all Robby's doing?" chuckled Olive. Lily's eyes brightened up.

"See? This is how much Dad loves you!"

Lily and Olive started laughing. They laughed so much

that other people around them turned to see what was happening at the counter table. When they saw a mother and a daughter laughing, holding each other's hand and a travel pamphlet, a smile broke across their faces, too.

After Olive made the payment and they left the restaurant, Lily insisted that she would come to Union Station with Olive to see her off. But Olive refused.

"What's the point of coming all the way to the station just to see me off?" said Olive. "We'll see each other soon, and you have other good stuff to do at home. And to tell you the truth," said Olive and took a deep breath. "It would make it hard for me to say goodbye if you come that far."

Seeing tears quickly welling up in Olive's eyes, Lily did not push further.

"Okay, Mom. But text me when you get home, okay? And we'll start discussing the trip once you are back. Remember - we haven't a moment to lose!" said Lily and tapped on her watch.

Olive laughed. "I will. But first, enjoy your birthday, my beautiful girl!"

They hugged for one last time. Then Olive turned and started to walk toward the tram stop. A tram was just arriving from behind her.

"Run, Mom! You can catch it!"

Lily's cheerful voice echoed over the heavy rolling sound of the metal wheels. Olive ran. When she reached the stop, she turned around once more before stepping onto the tram. And there she saw her beautiful daughter on her 24th birthday, standing tall and waving at Olive with the brightest smile on her face.

Epilogue

The room was dark except for the fire burning in the fireplace. The sun had just set, and it was snowing outside. Alan was sitting on the couch listening to the crackling sound of fire, deep in thought.

In a remote cabin like this, the silence of winter was particularly deep, suitable to spend the week before Christmas when there were many things to reflect upon. There was a manuscript of his newest book on the coffee table, which Alan had spent the afternoon reading and revising.

There was a sound of the lock turning from the hallway. Leila must have come back from her walk. A few minutes later, he heard the footsteps coming up along with a gentle clinking sound, and Leila appeared from the staircase.

"It's so warm in here!" She exclaimed. "Are you still working? Or can I join you for a tea?"

Alan smiled. "Tea would be nice."

Leila sat next to Alan and placed the tray of tea and lemon biscuits on the coffee table. "They're fresh. I baked them this afternoon."

"You were thinking of Olive, my dear." Alan said thoughtfully, looking at the lemon biscuits.

Leila smiled and took Alan's hand. Then she noticed the manuscript on the table.

"Can I have a look?"

Alan nodded. "I think it's ready now. I'm going to send it to my editor after Christmas."

Leila took the manuscript in her hands and flipped through the pages. There were many scenes that she recognized, which were now all beautifully contained on the pages. But there was one thing missing.

"Honey, where is the title?"

"I've been thinking about it this whole afternoon. And this is what I've decided on."

Alan took a pen from his pocket and wrote on the front page of the manuscript.

Olive's Diary.

Leila squeezed Alan's hand. Even in the limited light from the fire, Alan could see Leila's eyes shine like Lake Louise on a sunny summer day. "This is wonderful, honey."

Alan was glad that the room was dark because nobody could see how flushed his face was. "My dear, are you sure you're happy that I decided to write this book instead of you and Olive's childhood story?"

"Oh, most certainly," smiled Leila. "All my favourite people appear in the story. You, Olive, Robby, Lily, and our new friend Maple! It's a perfect gift to celebrate our 50th friendship anniversary. But even more than that, it makes such a special gift for Olive and Robby."

The two of them sipped the Earl Grey and took a few bites from the lemon biscuits. In the silence, they knew they were thinking of the same thing. Alan opened his mouth.

"Today is Olive and Robby's 21st anniversary, isn't it?"

"Yes, it is."

"I wonder how they're doing. I mean, Olive and Lily. Hope they're having a great time in Italy."

Leila jumped.

"What's the matter, dear?"

"Olive sent me a message this afternoon. I had completely forgot about it!" Leila reached for her phone. "I thought of reading it later with you."

Leila and Alan both straightened up on the couch and hovered over Leila's phone to read.

My dearest Leila,

Today marks 21st *years since Robby and I started our life together. Robby brought an incredible amount of love to my life, but there was one thing that I never fully embraced – his adventurous spirit. From Lily, I learned that he was planning a trip to Italy for our 20*th *anniversary. Though it's one year later, I'm happy to be able to tell him that I am doing his dream trip with our beloved Lily.*

Who would've thought that I was capable of travelling overseas? I didn't until I tried!

And it's wonderful. Every day, Lily and I are discovering new scenery, new people, and new insight into our life. I'm also learning a lot about my daughter as she shares her thoughts with me. Everything about this trip is bliss.

We'll be on our way back home in two days. I cannot wait to tell you everything about our trip over your delicious lemon biscuits (and Christmas meal)!

So much love from your friend of 50 years, Olive

There was a photograph attached to the email. "Look, how

happy they are!" Leila pointed to the photo as she blinked away her tears.

Olive and Lily were standing on a seaside in their jackets. In the late afternoon sunlight, with the background of white waves caressing the sand beach, the faces of a mother and a daughter were beaming like two bright stars.

"What a year it has been for them."

"Indeed," said Alan thoughtfully. "But it all turned out well, didn't it? Olive and Lily making a trip to Italy - it's a beginning of something new and wonderful."

"If only Robby could see them."

"Oh, I'm sure he is watching," said Alan, his eyes sparkling upon thinking of his friend. "He must be having a lot of fun right now following every step of Olive and Lily's trip."

The two of them laughed. Sitting in the comfort of the fire, the tea and the biscuits, their thoughts momentarily travelled to the seaside in the picture, watching and listening to the sound of waves next to Olive and Lily.

Then in the distance, they heard a sound. It was a grandfather's clock striking six in the hallway.

"We'd better get moving, honey," said Leila getting to her feet. "Today is our last night in this cabin, remember? We still have some packing and cleaning to do."

"Yes, my dear," answered Alan, watching Leila collect the teacups swiftly. Her quick movement reminded him that the quiet week of reflection was coming to an end.

"Maple and Kevin are coming to our house tomorrow evening, am I right?" asked Alan.

"That's right. And Olive and Lily will be arriving the evening after."

Alan nodded. "It's going to be a big gathering this year."

"Well, I'm quite ready for that. Aren't you?" beamed Leila as she made her way to the staircase with the tray in her hands.

"Olive and Lily are coming back from Italy. Maple and Kevin are now part of our extended family. Tell me, what can be more exciting than that?"

After Leila went downstairs, Alan sat in front of the fire alone for some more time. In the dark room with the remaining scent of tea and biscuits, as he thought back on the year's journey for them all, including himself, a smile appeared on his face, then tears, followed by a laughter. When he finally stood up to join Leila for the meal preparation downstairs, there was new lightness in the air. Alan skipped down the stairs with his new manuscript under his arm, gently humming 'Carol of the Bells'.

Acknowledgments

In December 2019, I was in Rome, Italy, on a three-month research stay as part of my PhD program. It was a long enough stay for me to live a disciplined life of a student - working on my thesis project daily at the national library near my airbnb that I had fallen in love with - and at the same time utilize my weekends to fully enjoy all the touristic activities one could do in the famous ancient city of Europe.

One sunny weekend of early December, I joined a day trip to Tivoli to visit Hadrian's Villa and Villa d'Este. They are both world-famous historic villas, one from the 2nd century Roman Empire and the other from the 16th century Renaissance Rome. Although they may appear to be irrelevant to each other, Villa d'Este was inspired by Hadrian's Villa - as I learned from our tour guide - and the significant portion of its building materials was recycled from the ruin of Hadrian's Villa.

During this exciting day trip, we made a stop at a traditional restaurant near Villa d'Este for lunch break. We were told to sit wherever we liked, enjoy the lunch, then come back to the group an hour later.

We were a group of about twelve people, but apart from me, everybody was participating as a couple or as a group. I was the only solo participant. Naturally, people sat at tables with their own travel companions and I was left alone. Though I usually didn't mind eating on my own, since it was a rare occasion to socialize with other travellers over a meal, I preferred to sit with somebody. As I looked around the room, feeling awkward like a transferred student, one middle-aged lady waived at me with a smile to join her table.

She was a traveller from Boston, US, and her daughter sitting next to her seemed to be close to my age. As I sat at their table, I felt as if being welcomed to a family gathering. There was an instant feeling of warmth exchanged between us.

We enjoyed the most delicious lunch together and talked about each other's trip and life. The daughter was doing her master's study in Washington D.C. and it was their first trip abroad together. As I listened to their story, I thought to myself how wonderful that they had planned the trip to nurture their relationship. Certainly, I had never done anything like that with my own mother.

The mother said that she was a librarian.

"How cool!" I exclaimed. "I've always loved libraries, but I have never met a librarian friend in my life!"

She also had a remarkable friend and colleague, who was mentioned several times in our conversation. Apparently, this friend was very talkative, and when she gave them a call the night before their flight to wish them a good journey, she kept talking for hours and they finally had to make her understand that they needed to have a good night sleep before the trip.

"How unique!" I exclaimed again. "What a remarkable friend you have!"

The daughter spoke less compared to her mother, but I could feel that she also had a lot to share about her life. At one point, she mentioned to me that she and her friend were planning a trip to Japan for the summer 2020. It was a relevant topic since I had earlier said that I was planning to visit my family in Japan in August. The moment she spoke of her trip plan, her mother could not hide her surprise.

"But you didn't tell me anything about it!"

"Mom, you might have stopped me from going if I had told you." The daughter said gently but firmly. "You would have worried."

The mother was silent for a second, then opened her mouth.

"Well, that would have been me five years ago, but I would no longer interfere with your plan since you are an adult!"

I looked at both of them and recalled my own relationship with my mother. I could totally understand what kind of feeling this girl was talking about. My mother worried every time I shared my travel plan with her including the one to move to Ottawa to do my PhD study. *So, it's not just me,* I thought to myself, *this tricky tension of a mother-daughter relationship is a shared phenomenon!*

At the end of our lunch, the mother suggested that her daughter and I should exchange our contact information so that we could stay in touch. Of course, we were eager to do so! I gave the girl my email address and felt happy that we would be in touch. The girl promised me to drop me a message later.

In the afternoon, when we visited Villa d'Este, I walked with this mother and the girl. We were guided through beautiful rooms and corridors and came to a spacious balcony with a most gorgeous view of the whole village and valley. Wanting to do something to celebrate the beautiful trip of this girl and her mother, I offered to take their photo with the breathtaking view of the valley in the background. As I clicked the photo, they both beamed with a smile that was as radiant as the sun shining above them.

I was looking forward to sending the photo to the girl, but it never happened. The email address I gave the girl must have been misspelled since I never heard back from her and I never knew her contact address. I regretted my mistake so much, but there was no crying over spilled milk.

Thus the beautiful picture of the girl and her mother remained on my computer. I could never forget about them and always thought of them and wondered how their lives might have continued after that trip.

Then, one day after more than a year since the trip, the idea of *Olive's Diary* came to me. My longing to celebrate the mother and the daughter that I met in Tivoli by sending them their beautiful photo had called in the story of Olive and Lily. Even though the story of Olive and Lily is based on my imagination and is certainly different from the one of the mother and the girl I met in Tivoli, I believe that *Olive's Diary* does capture some universal emotions experienced between a mother and a daughter. And it is my wish to celebrate the journey and love of each mother-daughter pair who are going through their own unique set of difficulties and challenges.

I still dream of reuniting with these two remarkable souls I met in Tivoli, thanking them for that beautiful lunch time, and hearing more of their life stories.

I would like to thank my editor Sonny Marr for her most insightful edits as well as the care with which she treated the story. *Olive's Diary* would not have come to its full life without her presence. I also thank my cover designer Ashley Santoro for creating this inspiring cover design that captures the essence of the story, and my formatter Nola Li Barr for putting all the pieces together into this beautiful book format.

This book was written with the support of the Self-Publishing School and its community of people. I would like to express my special thanks to my coach Barbara Hartzler, who has followed my footsteps and held me accountable throughout my first publishing journey. Without SPS and Barbara's constant presence, this book would probably not have crossed the finish line since the journey of writing and publishing a book can be confusing and lonely for a first-time author.

Finally, I would like to thank my dear friends and families in Ottawa, in Japan, and in different parts of the world who are always excited to hear my voice through each story that I write. The life I share with you is the very treasure of my life, and I am truly grateful for having a way to celebrate it.

About the Author

Maiko Serizawa is a story writer and mathematician living in Ottawa, the capital city of Canada. What inspired her onto the journey of story writing was the early loss of her one and only younger brother at the age of six. At the time, she wrote a series of adventure stories starring her brother and discovered the healing power in writing. As a writer, she is most fascinated by the subtle stories found in our day-to-day life. She loves visiting coffee shops for writing, and *Olive's Diary* is inspired by her favourite café in Ottawa and her years of experience at different coffee shops around the world.

You can connect with her on her website www.maple-and-olive.com where she keeps a daily blog of short stories. She is also a host of the weekly show *Maiko's Story Photograph Podcast* available on Spotify and Apple Podcasts.

Letter To My Reader

My dearest Reader,

Thank you so much for picking up this book, and moreover, reading it to the end!

It's my deepest joy that I got to deliver this story to you.

I'm now so curious to know what you have to share about the book! Please take a moment to leave a review on your local Amazon so that I can find your thoughts there. Your feedback will be a gift for me in my future writing journey as well as for those who are going to read the book after you.

To personally stay in touch with me and join my future book journey, follow the link below to become part of my Book Community! In addition to my book updates, you'll get a weekly Story Letter from me about my life and some fun insights into our life!

https://www.subscribepage.com/olivesdiarybonuschapter

When you join, you'll receive a bonus chapter of *Olive's Diary* as my welcome gift. I truly look forward to welcoming you there!

Thank you, thank you, and thank you for your presence from the bottom of my heart!

With much love from Ottawa, Maiko Serizawa